MONTHLY MAGICKAL RECORD

A 31-DAY SPELL JOURNAL
FOR MODERN WITCHES

KELLY CREE & JESSICA MULLEN

? sch◣◢l of
✦ life design

MICROCOSM PUBLISHING
PORTLAND, OR

Monthly Magickal Record: A 31-Day Spell Journal for Modern Witches
© Jessica Mullen and Kelly Cree 2021
This edition © Microcosm Publishing, 2021
This is Microcosm #579
ISBN #*9781648410406*

First Edition, September 14, 2021

Microcosm Publishing
2752 N Williams Ave
Portland, OR 97227
(503)799-2698

OTHER ZINES, BOOKS, STICKERS, PATCHES, PINS, POSTERS, T-SHIRTS, DVDS, & MORE:
WWW.MICROCOSM.PUB

To join the ranks of high-class stores that feature Microcosm titles, talk to your rep: In the U.S. **Como** (Atlantic), **Fujii** (Midwest), **Book Travelers West** (Pacific), **Turnaround** in Europe, **Manda/UTP** in Canada, **New South** in Australia, and **GPS** in Asia, India, Africa, and South America. We are sold in the gift market by **Faire**.

Did you know that you can buy our books directly from us at sliding scale rates? Support a small, independent publisher and pay less than Amazon's price at www.Microcosm.Pub

Global labor conditions are bad, and our roots in industrial Cleveland in the 70s and 80s made us appreciate the need to treat workers right. Therefore, our books are MADE IN THE USA.

Library of Congress Cataloging-in-Publication Data

Names: Cree, Kelly, 1983- author. | Mullen, Jessica, author.
Title: Monthly magickal record : a 31-day spell journal for modern witches
  / Kelly Cree & Jessica Mullen, School of Life Design.
Description: Portland : Microcosm Publishing, [2021] | Summary: "The School
  of Life Design Monthly Magickal Record is a 158-page monthly planner and
  interactive book of spells. Your thoughts create your reality, and your
  words are the spells that bring thought to life. With systematic
  clarity, the Monthly Magickal Record unveils the exact process of how
  your words become flesh. There are 31 pages of the Daily Ritual, where
  you can chronicle your divination readings, pre-pave your experiences
  and manifest your desires. Between each Daily Ritual is a different
  spell for stepping into your power as god in human form. Also included
  are six weeks of calendar pages for participating in time-based
  consensus reality. Designed for modern witches, conscious creators, and
  mindful magicians alike, this journal empowers users to make magick a
  daily practice"-- Provided by publisher.
Identifiers: LCCN 2021010608 | ISBN 9781648410406 (trade paperback)
Subjects: LCSH: Religious calendars--Wicca. | Witchcraft. | Magic.
Classification: LCC BF1572.F37 C74 2021 | DDC 133.4/3--dc23
LC record available at https://lccn.loc.gov/2021010608

TABLE OF CONTENTS

MAGICK
is the
METHOD
of SCIENCE
and the
AIM of
RELIGION

ALEISTER CROWLEY

introduction

This book was born out of a desire to refresh and revise our popular title, the *Monthly Manifestation Manual*. With updated calendars, a brand new Daily Ritual spread, and 31 unique exercises, the *Monthly Magickal Record* combines the utility of a day planner with the witchcraft of a modern *Book of Shadows*.

The founder of modern magick, Aleister Crowley, believed in a scientific approach to mysticism, recommending recording spiritual progress in a diary. It is an effective method for mastering your magickal practice by helping you recognize patterns in cause and effect. This book will help you learn what magickal concepts work for you.

There is no prerequisite for the *Monthly Magickal Record*. If you have already experienced the *Monthly Manifestation Manual*, you will find this book takes what you learned from the *MMM* and pushes it further.

Inspired by Don Miguel Ruiz's *The Four Agreements*, we named each new exercise a "spell" to emphasize the power of words. Words are spells we cast on the world, and what we say and think completely influences reality as we know it. Every single utterance from your consciousness affects your experience, so we created this journal for harnessing, organizing, and wielding that power.

Magick works best when you make it a daily practice, but there is no requirement to use this record every day. Sometimes, stepping away from spellwork is necessary for manifestation. When you forget you ever wanted it, you find it's already yours.

However, there is a Daily Ritual spread and companion exercise for each day of a 31-day month. Weaving this book into a deliberate daily practice reveals the dimension of magick and synchronicity, training your attention into the perfection of the present moment.

We made this book because we know the satisfaction of transmuting pain into love. Every negative aspect of your life can now bring you the pleasure of feeling better and all the manifestations that come with a good mood. Your mood is your work, because it is the way you feel that attracts your circumstances. Let the *Monthly Magickal Record* help you feel the best you've ever felt, and before long your reality will appear as heaven on earth!

THIS IS THE MAGICKAL RECORD OF

THIS MONTH I INTEND

_____

_____

_____

HOW TO USE THIS BOOK

MONTHLY CALENDAR
On page 7 you'll find a blank month-at-a-glance calendar. You can start the month at any date you wish, and this calendar can be used for any month. Pencil in the dates of your 31-day timeframe, and use this calendar to keep track of bills, important dates, and appointments.

WEEKLY CALENDARS
The 31 unique exercises in this journal are broken up into 5 weeks or chapters. At the beginning of each chapter is a 7-day calendar that can start on any day you need it to. Here is where to keep track of your meals, what you're grateful for, and your to-not-give-a-fuck-about list, which asks you to imagine what it would feel like to truly let go of needing to check items off a list to feel good. When you do not give a fuck if you get something done, you will find the universe makes arrangements for you.

DAILY RITUAL
Filling out your Daily Ritual page each day will help you get your energy in alignment for doing your spellwork. It's important that you perform your Daily Ritual prior to the spell to get the most of out your spellcasting. If you don't have time to do both, always opt for the Daily Ritual and return to the spell at a later time. Your Daily Ritual will always give you the framework you need to tune your energy; the spellwork helps you consciously direct that energy.

31 UNIQUE SPELLS
Between each Daily Ritual spread is a different mind training activity. Visualization exercises open your imagination to manifesting and healing powers. Mental code repetition trains new neural pathways in your brain, resulting in new patterns of thought. Gratitude and appreciation activities reveal that what you notice, you get more of. Pages practicing channeling strengthen your connection to infinite intelligence. Deep dives into the concept of awareness explore how simply watching your thoughts brings about peace. Several spells command the power of intention, and the remaining practices ask you to transmute negative experiences into positive expectation.

These games of consciousness incorporate magick into your daily life, uncovering the peace in your mind and joy in your heart. They remind you that life is not serious and your power lies in your perspective. Many spells include prompts for rating your mood before and after completion, so you can objectively gauge the effectiveness of each method.

Each individual spell was inspired by a different thought leader. Explore their work deeper via the "Further Reading" portion of each spread.

SUNDAY	MONDAY	TUESDAY	WEDNESDAY	THURSDAY	FRIDAY	SATURDAY
						1
2	3	4	5	6	7	8
9	10	11	12	13	14	15
16	17	18	19	20	21	22
23	24	25	26	27	28	29
30	31					

MONTH OF _January_

DAILY RITUAL

The Daily Ritual includes divination, spell casting, pre-paving, intention setting, gratitude, and visualization—everything you may need to practice conscious creation, mindfulness, and manifestation. It's best to complete this spread early in your day to focus your creative energy, but it can be just as effective to center yourself before going to bed. Fit it into your schedule wherever you most need an energetic restart.

DATE, TIME, MOON PHASE, & DREAM
This physical-world time tracking is useful for identifying patterns and synchronicities. There is also space to record a dream, whether it came to you in sleep last night or a daydream you can't stop imagining.

DIVINATION
Ask your question. This could be about love, money, health, work, family, or something specific. The next three blocks provide space for recording the answers you receive in divination. Use your tarot decks, your runes, your pendulum, your tea leaves, or whatever else you may have at your disposal. Consult the oracles and note the answers. You can leave the question blank to receive more general messages, or wait to fill out the blocks until you see signs in your daily life.

CAST A SPELL
We borrow a prompt from Bashar, which helps us immediately begin living in our desired reality. "I am switching to the version of reality I prefer. In the reality I prefer..." and write your reality as you want it to be. Manifestation is just a shift in perception, and this spell casting can bring about immediate results. This spell is a top priority, as it selects the seeds of thought you most want to nurture today.

PRE-PAVING
This is a technique created by Abraham-Hicks, in which you imagine a future event going exactly the way you want it to go, in order to mold your expectation and thus reality. First, name the event. Then write down the best circumstances that could happen before the event. What's the best that can happen during? And finally, how do you want to feel after the event? This exercise works so well, you won't want to go a day without it.

INTENTIONS, PRAYERS, DECLARATIONS OF LOVE, AND FORGIVENESS

These actions direct our energy, ask for help from the universe, tune ourselves to the highest vibration, and let go of our petty, ego-driven complaints.

GRATITUDE IN ADVANCE

This powerful prompt asks you to say thank you for the things you want, as if you already have them. That is the core of manifestation—acting as if you already have the thing you want, and really feeling as good as if you did. Think about what you want, then start expressing your gratitude for it, as if you already had it. This gets you in the feeling place of having what you want, thus making you a magnet for it to come. Think of this as a magickal shopping list. If you don't have much on your list, de-prioritize this section and come back to it when you feel strong desire.

HOW YOU WANT TO FEEL

Everything we want to manifest, we want because we think it will make us feel better. What if we just chose to feel that good first? We wouldn't need the manifestation! Identify what it is that you really want to feel, and take a moment to practice what it would feel like to feel that way. You don't need anything outside of yourself to be happy; it can all be generated from within. This is one of the most important prompts of the Daily Ritual, because how you feel dictates what you see.

NOTES & EPIPHANIES

If meditation is something you do, there is space for insights and epiphanies. Otherwise the space can be used to make notes about your rituals, magick, or daily experiences.

CONSULT YOUR GUIDES

This blank box is perfect for doodling and intuiting. Quiet your mind and listen for what advice you hear. You can try drawing with your non-dominant hand to see what your subconscious wants to tell you. Alternatively, you can draw a vision you've had, or a visualization of something you want. Let this be a space to uncover your inner wisdom, however it may come about. No pressure to complete this section; the guides always have perfect timing.

DATE

2-27-20

DREAM

IN the Texas SUN

TIME 11:11 AM

13%

MOON PHASE

● ◐ ◼ ◐ ○ ○ ○ ○ ◑ ◑ ◐

QUESTION

How can il be more PRESENT?

ANSWERS	ANSWERS	ANSWERS
FUCK IT! All that matters is how you feel RIGHT NOW!	The Rebel / the Emperor Live your TRUTH!	The High PRIESTESS all Knowledge is WITHIN. Sense the SECRET.

CAST A SPELL

I'M SWITCHING TO THE VERSION OF REALITY I PREFER. IN THE REALITY I PREFER...

I love myself! This moment is enough! Life already is the way il want it to be!

PRE-PAVE

EVENT TITLE

Phone call w/ V

BEFORE great mood! count to 10k! I let the moment be enough! practice presence.

DURING synchronicity! epiphanies! connection! love!

AFTER THANK YOU!

I INTEND
to be PRESENT
+
PLAYFUL!

I PRAY
to stay sober
+
HELP!

I LOVE
PERFECT TiMing
NMRK MIRACLES
PASSive income!

GRATITUDE in ADVANCE

I'M SO GRATEFUL
OUR BOOK is a best-seller!

safe travels

new music!

Rent + bills are paid!

best birthday ever!

Flawless VICTORY car rental

new tattoo!

CHICKENS! + garden

wild horses write new book!

TRAMPOLINE PARK!

I FORGIVE
myself for
going
unconscious

I WANT TO FEEL ENthusiasm!

NOTES & EPIPHANIES
THANK YOU is the
vibration of SUCCESS!

THIS IS IT!

VISIONS & GUIDES

SETTING
INTENTIONS

....

The goal of magick is to prove to yourself the power you have over your life experience. The first step to honing and intensifying that power is to believe it is possible. Your ability to affect change on your existence is directly related to how much ability you think you have.

Not only does being in the mindset of a conscious creator require imagination, it also requires release. In order to exact control over your existence, you must release all control. Contrary to what you've been taught all your life, your control is in letting go.

This chapter will help you focus your attention on the version of reality you're creating. It will also help you be at peace with whatever life creates, knowing it's always in your favor. In this chapter, you'll learn that conscious creation has very little to do with physical action and everything to do with your state of being.

DAY Monday DATE Jan 3	TO NGAF ABOUT	GRATITUDE
MEALS B: pound cake (+ coffee L: Sandwich D: Cauliflower rice + beans	☑ Self imposed deadlines ☑ imposter syndrome ☐ the future (outside of ☐ _____ ☐ _____	a great job! My fiance my control)

DAY Tuesday DATE Jan 4	TO NGAF ABOUT	GRATITUDE
MEALS B: Cereal + coffee L: leftovers, hummus, Carrots D: fried rice + salad	☑ being overwhelmed ☑ other people's timelines ☑ awkward situations ☑ putting myself out there ☐ _____	My body's abilities pain relief after exercising

DAY Wednesday DATE 1.5	TO NGAF ABOUT	GRATITUDE
MEALS B: Cereal + Coffee L: leftover rice D: Mac + Cheese	☑ rejection ☑ things out of my control ☐ _____ ☐ _____ ☐ _____	Getting up + working out Still being able to move Motivation

DAY Thursday DATE 1.6	TO NGAF ABOUT	GRATITUDE
MEALS B: fiber bar	☐ the negative ☐ thoughts about ☐ my body ☐ my physical ☐ limitations	Noticable mental, emotional, and physical improvement

GRATITUDE	TO NGAF ABOUT	DAY
		DATE
	☐ _____	**MEALS**
	☐ _____	
	☐ _____	
	☐ _____	
	☐ _____	

GRATITUDE	TO NGAF ABOUT	DAY
		DATE
	☐ _____	**MEALS**
	☐ _____	
	☐ _____	
	☐ _____	
	☐ _____	

GRATITUDE	TO NGAF ABOUT	DAY
		DATE
	☐ _____	**MEALS**
	☐ _____	
	☐ _____	
	☐ _____	
	☐ _____	

NOTES

DREAM Rebecca abandonned me @
our college / shopping mall / Ellis Island?

1/3/21

TIME 10:57AM

New Moon 1.4%

MOON PHASE
◨ ◐ ◑ ○ ○ ○ ○ ○ ○

QUESTION

How can I show up everyday!

ANSWERS	ANSWERS	ANSWERS
Make "extra" self-care tasks + obligations low-hanging fruit	Stay hydrated	Get the hardest stuff out of the way in the morning, when you have the most energy

CAST A SPELL

I'M SWITCHING TO THE VERSION OF REALITY I PREFER. IN THE REALITY I PREFER...

Apathy doesn't exist! But I do know how to relax

PRE-PAVE

EVENT TITLE
Social Media Call @ 3PM

16

BEFORE
meditate
have stats
& links ready
drink water

DURING
fluid, intelligible thoughts
not minimizing my accomplishments
praise
araise

AFTER
solid
capable
accomplished
deserving

I INTEND
TO GET OFF
MY ASS

I PRAY
For my mother
& Gigi's health

I LOVE
watching my savings
account grow.
Spending time w/ Alex
making us dinner

**GRATITUDE
IN ADVANCE**

I'M SO GRATEFUL
• for my slim, healthy,
powerful body.
• For my successful
podcast + all the
opportunities that
come from it.
• for our beautiful,
spacious RH'
apartment
• to be back in BK
w/ Alex

I FORGIVE
MYSELF

**I WANT
TO FEEL** Ethereal

NOTES & EPIPHANIES

Scanning up + down
my chakras is a great
body scan.

lean forward when I
meditate - is
his yearning

crown
<-- third eye
throat
— heart—
diaphragm
— sacral

VISIONS & GUIDES root

SPELL FOR
vision

Everything you see physically manifested began as a vision. The most powerful technology, the truest love, the beach-iest vacation all were born in someone's imagination. The imagination is the birthplace of all manifestations.

Have you ever looked up and realized you have what you once wanted? It can be so easy to get distracted by always looking for the next manifestation that we forget to be conscious of all that we have already manifested for ourselves. In the midst of everyday life, it can also be difficult to remember to set aside time to think about what it is we *do* want instead of what we *don't*.

As you begin this journal, take some time to think about what you truly want. Give birth to it in your mind's eye. It's alive! Throughout the course of the next 30 days (or however you long you choose to use this Magickal Record), you will nurture and grow these newborn desires by nurturing yourself. As time goes on, if you start to wonder if your vision is manifesting into reality, don't. Know that it's already done. After you finish all of the exercises, return to this page and take note of all that was created in the background while you focused on harmonizing with the energy within.

instructions

For each category on this vision board, write, draw, or paste pictures of what you want. Be general if you have to, or be specific if you know exactly what you want. As you fill out this page, practice feeling what it would feel like to receive the things you want. There is no limit to what you can create in this life, so dream big! After you've completed the page, do your best to let the desires go and trust they're on the way.

FURTHER READING

ASK AND IT IS GIVEN BY ESTHER AND JERRY HICKS

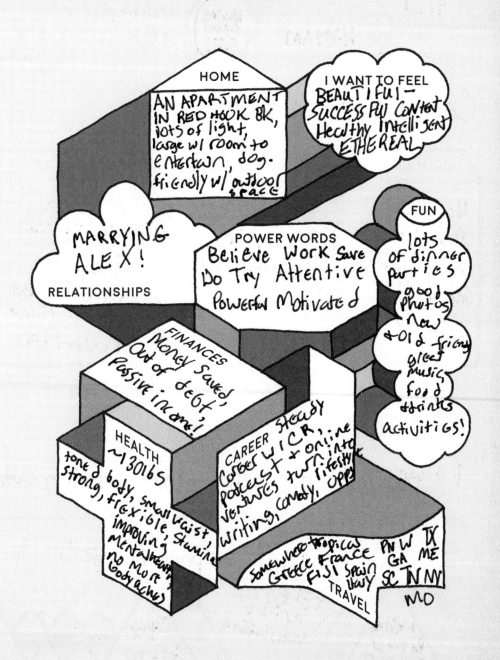

1/4/21

QUESTION | TIME 11:09AM | Waxing Crescent 5.3% | MOON PHASE ● ◐ ○ ○ ○ ○ ○ ○ ◑ ○

Can I have it all?

ANSWERS

No, but you can have enough and that's great

ANSWERS

Yes! within reason

ANSWERS

As long as "all" includes time for rest + reflection + recreation

CAST A SPELL

I'M SWITCHING TO THE VERSION OF REALITY I PREFER. IN THE REALITY I PREFER...

I always make an effort without burning out

PRE-PAVE

EVENT TITLE

Social Report for Both

20

BEFORE Meditate Review all report data. Draft!

DURING Patience Clarity Understanding

AFTER Capable Go-to girl for Audience Growth

I INTEND to get into a regular workout routine again

I PRAY my mom's bloodwork is all clear

I LOVE the feeling I get after exercise

GRATITUDE IN ADVANCE

I'M SO GRATEFUL to be strong, fit, and flexible.

For my sense of style

for high self-esteem, self-worth, + confidence

For my inner + outer beauty

I FORGIVE myself Pete Davidson?

I WANT TO FEEL BEAUTIFUL

NOTES & EPIPHANIES I am good at my job!

I would draw the cardinal or hawk/falcon that landed in the yard but that is... not happening

CALMING ANXIETY

A potent indicator of alignment is your breath. We try to force things into being all day long; meanwhile our breath is breathing itself in the background. Our hearts stay beating without our interference. Life is always living us, not the other way around.

In this exercise, notice your breath but don't try to control it. Observe it, don't force it. Notice when it is coming in by writing, "Breathing in, I know I am breathing in," in the space provided. Write, "Breathing out, I know I am breathing out," as you exhale. Appreciate how the breath breathes you. Continue to watch this process and write along with it until the page is full.

Now you are equipped to face your day with the knowledge that every-thing in life is unfolding as naturally as your breath. You're not in charge, so you can just observe. You don't have to get involved or make anything happen. You can watch from above instead of being tossed about by the ups and downs of life.

It's all written in the breath. Life as we know it is a series of polarities: on and off, in and out, light and dark. It is this duality we came to frolic in and explore. But when you're in an ebb in life and want to get back to the flow, return to this breath practice to help you remember what you know. When you know what you don't want, you know what you do want. The opposite of your experience is already created, and you can use your breath to guide you to that opposite side of the wave. From anxiety to tranquility, your breath is your constant connection to source.

On a scale of 1-10, rate how anxious you are before and after completing this exercise. Did it help?

BEFORE   4   AFTER   2

FURTHER READING

HOW TO RELAX BY THICH NHAT HANH

Breathing in,
I know I am breathing in

Breathing out, I know I am breathing
out. Breathing in. Breathing out.
Breathing in breathing out breathing
in breathing out in out in out in out
in out in out in out in in out in out in out
breathing in, i know i am breathing in
in out in out in out in out in out in out
in out breathing in breathing out breathing in
breathing out breathing in breathing out in
in out breathing in breathing out out in
out breathing in out breathing in breathing
in out breathing in breathing out breathing
in breathing out in out in out
in out breathing in breathing out in
out breathing in breathing out breathing
in breathing out in breathing out in out
in breathing out breathing in breathing
out breathing in breathing out in
out breathing in breathing out
breathing in breathing out breathing in
breathing out in out in out in
out breathing in, I know I am
breathing in, breathing out I know
am breathing out in out in out
breathing in breathing out
breathing in breathing out in out in out
breathing in breathing   out in out in
out in out   in out   in out in
out in out in out

MENTAL CODES

DATE
. . . .
1.5

DREAM

I was dating a kardashian boy

TIME
12:31 PM

12.26
waxing
crescent

MOON PHASE
● ◉ ◐ ○ ○ ○ ◑ ◐ ●

QUESTION

How can I stay 'in the moment?

ANSWERS

Just being present

ANSWERS

Stop trying to plan

ANSWERS

Let the universe take the reigns

CAST A SPELL

I'M SWITCHING TO THE VERSION OF REALITY I PREFER. IN THE REALITY I PREFER...

I am fit, healthy, and successful

PRE-PAVE

EVENT TITLE

WASH DAY

BEFORE
bring all my supplies to other bathroom cue up a podcast or book

DURING
Detangle carefully scrub that scalp remove buildup

AFTER
be patient love the process

I INTEND

To engage in self-care practices that are important to me

I PRAY

Alex and I won't have to spend any more extended time apart

I LOVE

my face, hair, sense of style, and body shape

GRATITUDE IN ADVANCE

I FORGIVE

my mom's side of the family

I'M SO GRATEFUL

that I am effortlessly put-together. that I always have a flattering outfit for every occasion that I have the resources to take care of myself & others

I WANT TO FEEL

put-together

NOTES & EPIPHANIES

this is the first time alex and I have been alone since February and it's amazing. Every moment i've questioned us forever has been because of family tension & instability. he is my world.

VISIONS & GUIDES

SPELL FOR
thriving

Timothy Leary was an American psychologist and writer known for advocating for therapeutic use of LSD and other psychedelics. He popularized the phrase "Turn on, tune in, drop out" in 1966 to encourage people to welcome cultural change with the help of psychedelics. Turning on meant becoming sensitive to different levels of consciousness, tuning in meant to exist in harmony with the world, and dropping out meant to think for oneself and extricate oneself from hierarchies or institutions that one had involuntarily or unconsciously participated in.

We can get a glimpse of the magick of psychedelics with just a few words of intention. Knowing that consciousness, harmony, and free thinking are possible, we can choose them for ourselves right now. We can be the change we wish to see in the world by turning on, tuning in, and dropping out.

instructions

1. What are you conscious of? Is it your breathing, your surroundings, your thoughts, your body, or maybe a particularly potent truth? What are you aware of in this very moment?

2. What do you want to live in harmony with? Use this opportunity to contribute to a more peaceful planet, home life, or inner world.

3. What system, institution, or hierarchy have you unwillingly or unknowingly participated in, that you wish to step away from? The oil industry, politics, or maybe specific grooming habits? What have you been conditioned to do that is no longer serving you? Make the choice to step away right now and begin creating your own system of thriving.

FURTHER READING

TURN ON, TUNE IN, DROP OUT BY TIMOTHY LEARY
YOUR BRAIN IS GOD BY TIMOTHY LEARY

DREAM

1.6.21

TIME **9:15am**

waxing cresent 19.1%.

MOON PHASE
● ◐ ◑ ○ ○ ○ ◑ ○ ○

QUESTION

How can I improve further?

ANSWERS

Baby steps;
a little bit
a time.

ANSWERS

Keep doing
exactly what
you're doing

ANSWERS

Set tiny goals
& knock
them out of
the park.
tiny victories!

CAST A SPELL

I'M SWITCHING TO THE VERSION OF REALITY I PREFER. IN THE REALITY I PREFER...

my body can stretch, move, and dance
freely. I am not encumbered by pain or physicalities.

PRE-PAVE

EVENT TITLE

Go to the drug store

BEFORE — have all my info

DURING — communicate patiently & clearly w/ pharmacy. mention insurance!

AFTER — Prozac!

I INTEND to maintain this AM sense of ease throughout the day

I PRAY Alex's family resolves their bs in time

I LOVE tiny victories

GRATITUDE IN ADVANCE

I FORGIVE my grandma

I'M SO GRATEFUL for my body. I am thin & toned - healthy. I am free of creaky joints, tight ligaments, and physical limitations. Movement feels amazing. And looks amazing too.

I WANT TO FEEL free

NOTES & EPIPHANIES

there's a black horse next door

The black horse totem is an emblem of death and rebirth. Its purpose is to aid you in leaving unnecessary things behind and showing you new opportunities that await. For this, it is required to take a risk + have faith.

VISIONS & GUIDES

SPELL FOR
OVERCOMING BELIEFS

Is there something you want reeeeeally bad, but you don't see evidence of it in your life experience? Could it be that subconsciously (or maybe consciously), you have a core belief that is preventing that desire from manifesting? Maybe you don't believe it is possible or that you're worthy of receiving it?

This is known as resistance. If what animates life is energy, then *resistance* prevents that energy from flowing. No matter how truly, madly, or deeply you want something, the energy to create it can never coalesce when opposition to the manifestation is present. Often this resistance arises as a result of self-doubt, fear, or attachment. We think that we (or our situation) has to change before we can fulfill our deepest desires. Or maybe we are afraid of what will happen when the manifestation is real. When we bring light to the resistant thoughts preventing the manifestation, and appreciate that aspect of ourselves or our life experience, we transmute the resistance into amplification without ever having to change.

instructions

1. Write down what you want on the rope and then the "but" that always follows in the struggling pony. When you write this statement, feel for an emotional reaction. Did your energetic center feel like it embraced or resisted this statement? Record your resistance level in the space provided.

2. Appreciate the aspect of yourself that is preventing this desire from manifesting and write it in the free pony. Maybe you don't think you deserve it because you're lazy or because you were born to the wrong parents or because you never had parents or because society is against you. Take a moment to deeply appreciate that aspect of your life experience. Again, feel for an embrace or rejection of this statement. Record your resistance level now.

FURTHER READING

THE BIG LEAP BY GAY HENDRICKS

DREAM

Tried to dispose of a living (but frozen & action-sized) hum

1.7.21

TIME 12:41 pm (29.7 Waxing)

MOON PHASE

QUESTION

When will I feel stable?

ANSWERS

Soon.
You're trying
so hard

ANSWERS

When your
Alex can be
together full-time

ANSWERS

When you can
the stop
obsessing over
your body

CAST A SPELL

I'M SWITCHING TO THE VERSION OF REALITY I PREFER. IN THE REALITY I PREFER...

I have control

PRE-PAVE **EVENT TITLE**

Eyebrow Appt.

BEFORE
tell
alex you
have appointment
wash face

DURING
be honest.
acknowledge this
step in better
self-care

AFTER
Confidence!
get your
Prozac
while you're out

I INTEND

to make it through today.

I PRAY

tear Alex drives safe in the snow

I LOVE

sleep.

GRATITUDE IN ADVANCE

I'M SO GRATEFUL

I kept going

I FORGIVE

Alex for unitentionally drawing attention to my stretch marks

I WANT TO FEEL beautiful

NOTES & EPIPHANIES

I keep having dreams about burying small beings alive - first puppies, then an action figure - sized black man who was on the verge of freesing. Burial dreams - repressing xtreme emotional feelings, or trying to put an end to something that has been troubling you that has not fully run its course.

Struggling w/ Gigi's mortuity?

Black living action figure - trying to repress my blackness? Or I predicted Sidney Pointier's death.

VISIONS & GUIDES

SPELL FOR
mAnifESTInG

When you want something, it implies you don't have it. When you think to yourself, "I really want more income," you are affirming that you don't have enough income. You are creating a reality in which you don't have enough, perpetuating a lack mindset.

When you notice a desire, decide to choose it instead of want it. When you choose something, your thoughts align with having it. You can try thinking things like, "I am choosing more income," or, "I am so grateful for the money I make. I always have plenty." Your thoughts about the things you desire are creating your reality as you think them, so begin to choose the thoughts you want to be true.

After you switch from wanting to choosing, let the desire go and never think of it again. Your thoughts are constantly creating, and if you start wondering if your "choosing" worked, you're undoing the spell. You must stand firm in your knowing of your creative power. You no longer have to want the power to manifest what you want. You can choose to step into your power right now.

instructions

1. What do you want? Fill in the lines provided.

2. How does it feel to want it and not have it?

3. Choose instead of want. Finish the sentence, "I choose..."

4. How do you feel now that you've chosen it, instead of wanting it?

FURTHER READING

CONVERSATIONS WITH GOD BY NEALE DONALD WALSCH

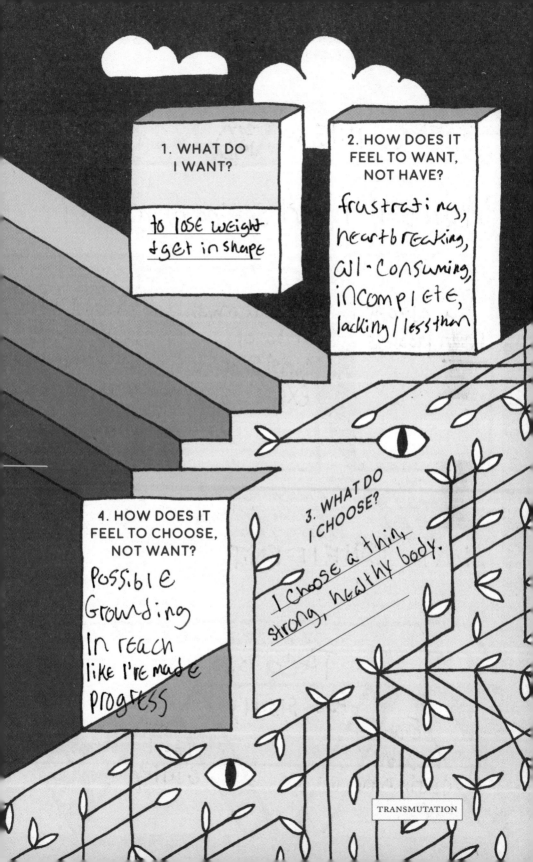

1.8.21

39% 1st quarter

MOON PHASE
● ● ◑ ◉ ○ ○ ○ ● ●

QUESTION

When will I start seeing progress?

ANSWERS

You already feel progress

ANSWERS

After a month or so of consistent exercise

ANSWERS

When I choose to acknowledge little things as progress

CAST A SPELL

I'M SWITCHING TO THE VERSION OF REALITY I PREFER. IN THE REALITY I PREFER...

I AM CONFIDENT

PRE-PAVE

EVENT TITLE
TACO Bell

BEFORE
Eat healthy during the day

DURING
Eat slowly

AFTER
Don't feel guilty

36

I INTEND

to keep moving

I PRAY

my Body lets me

I LOVE

my FIRE

GRatitude in ADVANCE

I FORGIVE

MYSELF

I'M SO GRATEFUL

For a circle of friends who understand I NEED TO BE ALONE RIGHT NOW.

I WANT
TO FEEL At home

NOTES & EPIPHANIES

Control is not the worst thing. In fact, it's something I need. But I also need balance

VISIONS & GUIDES

SPELL FOR
DETACHMENT

Have you ever noticed that when you haven't thought much about wanting something, it can be a lot easier to manifest than the things you've wanted and wanted and wanted? That's often because there exist deeper, more ingrained vibrations about the desire not being fulfilled. Your mind may be telling you, "You've wanted this for a long time and it still hasn't come; you're probably never going to get it." Or maybe you've built up so much awareness around the not having of it that it's hard for you to believe it's possible to have at all. Today, take your stale desire and release it for good with sigil magick.

instructions

1. Convert your deepest desire into a pictogram using the symbolic alphabet provided. Be sure not to write the desire in letters anywhere. You don't want to see the word(s) on the page, only the symbols. Your desire should be phrased as if you already have it, so if you want more friends, start with, "I have so many new friends." As you convert the desire into pictures, skip vowels and repeated letters.

2. Now, conjure the feeling of what it will feel like when this desire is fulfilled. Focus on feeling the feeling deeply. Don't get too lost in visualizing the *how*, rather stay centered in the emotion this manifestation brings about. Describe the feeling in the space provided.

Your desire is no longer a boulder in your gut that just keeps getting heavier. You've converted it to mere shapes and symbols and released it to the universe. Either it's on its way or you never needed it. Either way, you can choose to feel the feeling you wrote down any time you think about it. And sooner or later, the feeling of having it will replace the perception that you don't.

FURTHER READING

MAGICK: LIBER ABA, BOOK 4 BY ALEISTER CROWLEY

1.

2.

INTENTION

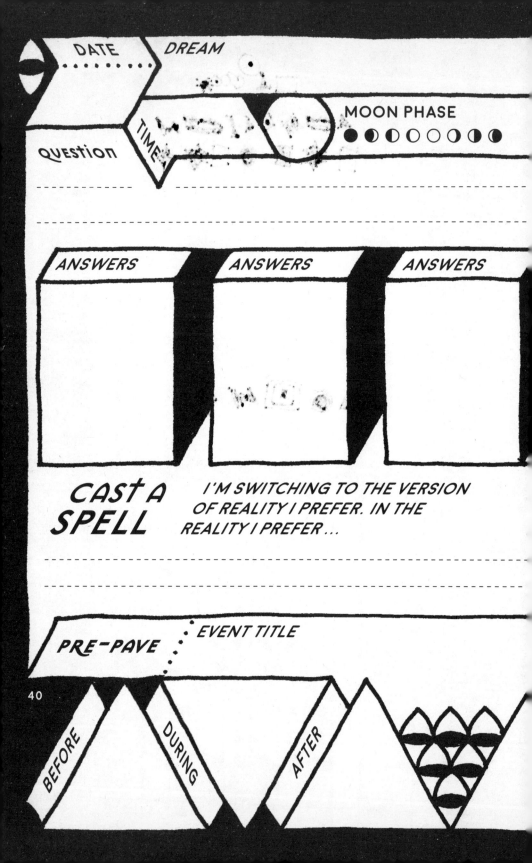

DATE

DREAM

MOON PHASE

Question

TIME

ANSWERS

ANSWERS

ANSWERS

CAST A SPELL

I'M SWITCHING TO THE VERSION OF REALITY I PREFER. IN THE REALITY I PREFER...

PRE-PAVE

EVENT TITLE

BEFORE

DURING

AFTER

I INTEND

I PRAY

I LOVE

GRATITUDE IN ADVANCE

I'M SO GRATEFUL

I FORGIVE

I WANT TO FEEL

NOTES & EPIPHANIES

VISIONS & GUIDES

SPELL FOR
LETTING GO

In his book *The Surrender Experiment*, Michael Singer tells the story of
the incredible amount of success he achieved in his life simply by saying
yes to everything that came his way. At one point, a woman decides to
build a home (!) on his property. While he was admittedly upset at first,
he eventually surrendered and helped her build the house. It turned out
that he loved building the house, so much so that he later started his
own wildly successful home-building company.

Life is always giving us gifts. Constantly. All day, every day. Most of the
time, we look at the gifts thinking, "Not what I wanted," or "Thanks,
but no thanks," or "Hell no, send this back!" However, when we begin
graciously accepting everything that comes our way, we lift the veil on
the illusion. We start seeing everything in life is happening for us, not
to us.

Fill the frame with the word "Yes." This exercise will help get your mind
running on that track and put your surrender on auto-pilot. Anything
that happens, say yes. Return to this page at the end of the day and
write down one thing you said yes to and how it affected your day.

One thing I said yes to:

_____

How it affected my day:

_____

FURTHER READING

THE SURRENDER EXPERIMENT BY MICHAEL SINGER

MENTAL CODES

EMPOWER YOURSELF

....

Now that you've learned that your power doesn't lie in physical control, it's time to start directing your non-physical energy. Your power of creation lies in your thoughts, beliefs, emotions, and expectations. In this chapter you will observe those aspects of your being and deepen your ability to select where you place your creative attention.

You're now in touch with your non-physical self and can unblock, gather, and focus that energy. With devotion to the practice, directing your energy will get easier. Your consciousness of the existence of this non-physical energy is your true power, so if directing your energy becomes too overwhelming, you can always sit back and let life do its work while you enjoy the ride.

In this chapter, you will see over and over that how you feel affects the world you live in. The exercises that follow will teach you how to *choose* how you feel, and thus *choose* the life you live.

DAY	TO NGAF ABOUT	GRATITUDE
DATE		
MEALS	☐ _____	
	☐ _____	
	☐ _____	
	☐ _____	
	☐ _____	

DAY	TO NGAF ABOUT	GRATITUDE
DATE		
MEALS	☐ _____	
	☐ _____	
	☐ _____	
	☐ _____	
	☐ _____	

DAY	TO NGAF ABOUT	GRATITUDE
DATE		
MEALS	☐ _____	
	☐ _____	
	☐ _____	
	☐ _____	
	☐ _____	

DAY	TO NGAF ABOUT	GRATITUDE
DATE		
MEALS	☐ _____	
	☐ _____	
	☐ _____	
	☐ _____	
	☐ _____	

GRATITUDE	TO NGAF ABOUT	DAY
		DATE
	☐ _____	**MEALS**
	☐ _____	
	☐ _____	
	☐ _____	
	☐ _____	

GRATITUDE	TO NGAF ABOUT	DAY
		DATE
	☐ _____	**MEALS**
	☐ _____	
	☐ _____	
	☐ _____	
	☐ _____	

GRATITUDE	TO NGAF ABOUT	DAY
		DATE
	☐ _____	**MEALS**
	☐ _____	
	☐ _____	
	☐ _____	
	☐ _____	

NOTES

DATE · · · · · · · · ·   DREAM

QUESTION   TIME

MOON PHASE
● ◐ ◑ ○ ○ ◑ ◐ ◑

ANSWERS	ANSWERS	ANSWERS

CAST A SPELL   I'M SWITCHING TO THE VERSION
OF REALITY I PREFER. IN THE
REALITY I PREFER ...

PRE-PAVE · · · · EVENT TITLE

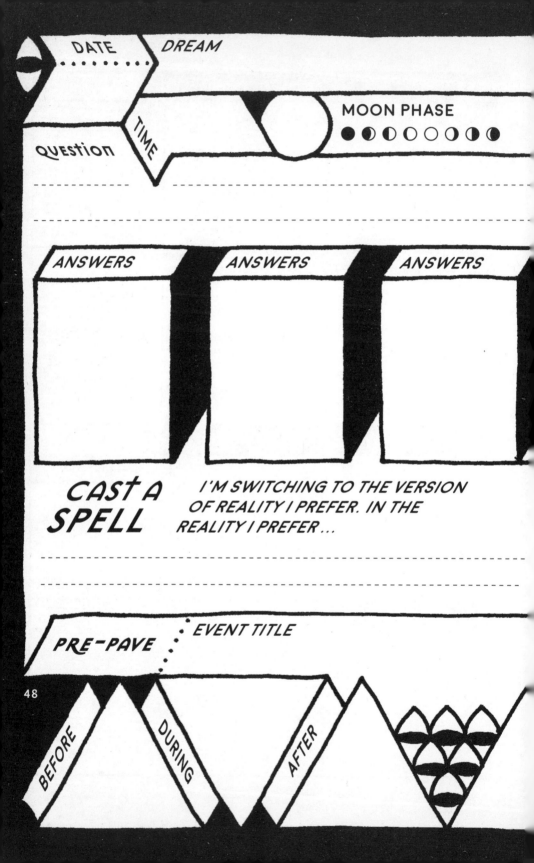

48

BEFORE   DURING   AFTER

I INTEND

I PRAY

I LOVE

GRATITUDE
IN ADVANCE

I'M SO GRATEFUL

- -

- -

I FORGIVE

- -

- -

- -

- -

*I WANT
TO FEEL*

- -

- -

NOTES & EPIPHANIES

- -

- -

- -

- -

- -

- -

- -

- -

VISIONS & GUIDES

SPELL FOR

UNBLOCKiNG ENERGY

When you have a serious problem plaguing you, turn to chakra visualization. Your chakras are seven energy centers in your body through which your life force flows. When you have a blocked chakra, you may notice physical symptoms in your body, or experience related problems in your life experience. But it's a simple fix to get your energy flowing smoothly again.

Since your chakras are invisible, visualization is an easy way to "speak" to them. When you have a specific problem you'd like solved, go within, light up your chakras, and get the energy flowing again.

instructions

Set your intention. What do you want? Phrase your desire with gratitude in advance. For example, if you want a cure for a health problem, your intention can be, "Thank you for healing me." Whatever it is you want, think to yourself, "Thank you for _____," as if it has already happened, and write it in the space provided.

Visualize a ball of white light coming in through your crown chakra. Send this ball of light through all your chakras (crown, third eye, throat, heart, solar plexus, navel, and tailbone), lighting up each energy center from top to bottom. This balances the energy in your body and makes you a clear conduit. Try thinking, "Breathing in, I bring light into my crown chakra. Breathing out, I activate my crown chakra," and so on for each energy center.

Once your chakras are all lit up, spend a couple minutes feeling that energy flow while you focus on your intention. "Thank you for healing me. Thank you for healing me."

After your visualization, ground the energy by saying, "I ground this energy that hasn't been used. I return it to the earth. Thank you for helping me." Repeat this process 15 minutes a day for maximum results.

FURtHER READiNG

MAKING MAGICK BY EDAIN MCCOY

THANK YOU FOR

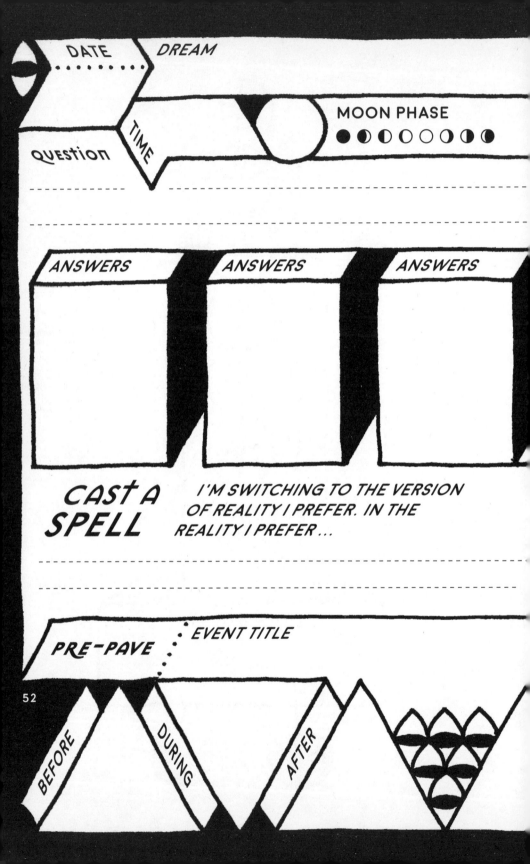

DATE

DREAM

Question

TIME

MOON PHASE

ANSWERS   ANSWERS   ANSWERS

CAST A
SPELL

I'M SWITCHING TO THE VERSION
OF REALITY I PREFER. IN THE
REALITY I PREFER ...

PRE-PAVE   EVENT TITLE

BEFORE   DURING   AFTER

I INTEND

I PRAY

I LOVE

GRATITUDE
IN ADVANCE

I'M SO GRATEFUL

- -

I FORGIVE

- -

- -

- -

- -

I WANT
TO FEEL

- -

- -

- -

NOTES & EPIPHANIES

- -

- -

- -

- -

- -

- -

- -

- -

VISIONS & GUIDES

SPELL FOR
POWER

Your power comes from your presence. When your attention is focused in the thin slice of *now* between the past and future, you have access to divine inspiration, your intuition, and universal intelligence. In the present moment, play becomes possible. In the present moment, your manifesting abilities are at their peak, because you aren't resisting the natural flow of well-being with your thoughts.

Silent counting is a technique for becoming present. It is the practice of consciously focusing on a stream of numbers in your head, instead of following the whirlwind trains of thought trying to scatter your attention. All day, every day, we are barraged with thoughts that can take our imaginations into the darkness. Silent counting gives us a way to remain present during our daily activities. Use silent counting to plug the attention drain of scattered thinking and charge your magickal power back up.

instructions
Count each box on the next page. Write numbers in the boxes, color them or draw dots in each shape. Keep count of your penstrokes in your mind. Try to reach 100, then start over. Aim to count to 10,000 in one day for supreme focus and empowerment.

FURTHER READING

THE POWER OF NOW BY ECKHART TOLLE

MENTAL CODES

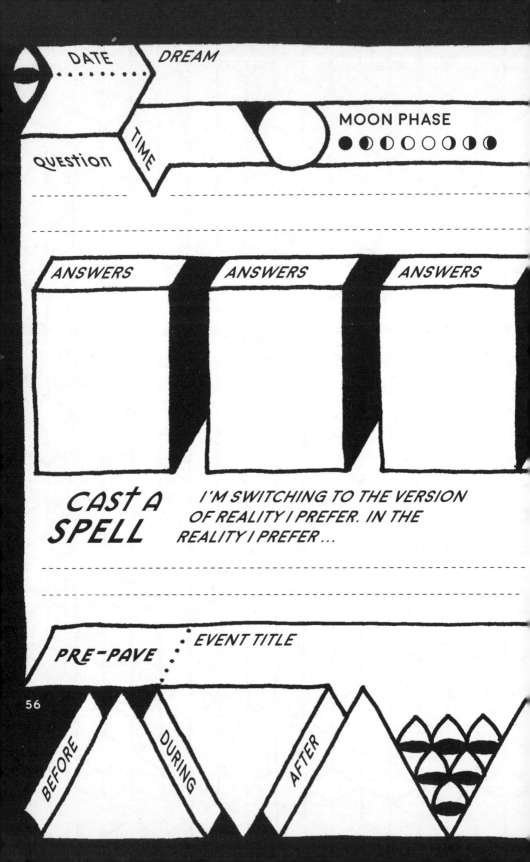

DATE
········

DREAM

Question

TIME

MOON PHASE
●◗◑◑○◐◑◐

ANSWERS

ANSWERS

ANSWERS

CAST A
SPELL

I'M SWITCHING TO THE VERSION
OF REALITY I PREFER. IN THE
REALITY I PREFER...

PRE-PAVE

EVENT TITLE

BEFORE

DURING

AFTER

I INTEND

I PRAY

I LOVE

GRATITUDE
IN ADVANCE

I'M SO GRATEFUL

- - - - - - - - - - - - - - - - - - - -

- - - - - - - - - - - - - - - - - - - -

I FORGIVE

- - - - - - - - - - - - - - - - - - - -

- - - - - - - - - - - - - - - - - - - -

- - - - - - - - - - - - - - - - - - - -

- - - - - - - - - - - - - - - - - - - -

*I WANT
TO FEEL*

- - - - - - - - - - - - - - - - - - - -

- - - - - - - - - - - - - - - - - - - -

NOTES & EPIPHANIES

- - - - - - - - - - - - - - - - - - - -

- -

- - - - - - - - - - - - - - - - - - - -

- - - - - - - - - - - - - - - - - - - -

- - - - - - - - - - - - - - - - - - - -

- - - - - - - - - - - - - - - - - - - -

- - - - - - - - - - - - - - - - - - - -

- - - - - - - - - - - - - - - - - - - -

- - - - - - - - - - - - - - - - - - - -

VISIONS & GUIDES

CVRING AILMENTS

> "The truth is to love yourself with the same intensity you would use to pull
> yourself up if you were hanging off a cliff with your fingers."
> KAMAL RAVIKANT

Do you love yourself? Do you intensely, authentically love yourself?
Unfortunately, a lot of people do not. We spend a lot of time hating on
ourselves in our minds–replaying sequences of times we've fucked up or
imagining potential future transgressions. We might even think about
how much we suck at life, how ugly or stupid we are, or what terrible
people we are.

Just as the outside world mirrors the contents of our thoughts and
emotions, so do our bodies. When you think, "I hate X about myself,"
or, "I'm a failure who will never amount to anything," those energies
manifest physically in our bodies as ailments. When you think, "I love
myself, I'm fabulous, and I deserve all the good that comes my way,"
that energy also manifests physically as well being. The two different
thought patterns produce noticeably different physiological and
emotional responses. Which one feels better?

Fill the space provided with the words "I love myself" and make an
effort to feel that love with the same intensity you would use if trying
to save your own life. Because that's what you're doing! When you say,
"I love myself," you allow healing into your life. You allow well-being
into your body. You allow yourself to thrive, flourish and bloom.

On a scale of 1-10, rate your level of ease before and after
completing this exercise. Do you feel more at ease?

BEFORE ☐ AFTER ☐

FVRTHER READING

LOVE YOURSELF LIKE YOUR LIFE DEPENDS ON IT BY KAMAL RAVIKANT
YOU CAN HEAL YOUR LIFE BY LOUISE HAY

MENTAL CODES

DATE · · · · · · DREAM

MOON PHASE
●●◑○○○○◐○

QUESTION   TIME

- -

- -

ANSWERS   ANSWERS   ANSWERS

CAST A
SPELL

*I'M SWITCHING TO THE VERSION
OF REALITY I PREFER. IN THE
REALITY I PREFER...*

- -

- -

PRE-PAVE · · · · · EVENT TITLE

BEFORE   DURING   AFTER

I INTEND

I PRAY

I LOVE

GRATITUDE
IN ADVANCE

I'M SO GRATEFUL

- -
- -
- -
- -
- -
- -
- -
- -
- -
- -
- -
- -

I FORGIVE

I WANT
TO FEEL

NOTES & EPIPHANIES

- -
- -
- -
- -
- -
- -
- -
- -

VISIONS & GUIDES

SPELL FOR
BLESSINGS

Though his work was met with significant criticism in the scientific community for not being "science," Dr. Masaru Emoto presents an intriguing and compelling hypothesis. He claimed that vibrational energies could change the physical structure of water. Therefore, since the human body is mostly water, your vibration affects your body. Emoto claimed that water to which loving words were spoken produced beautiful crystals when frozen, whereas when hateful words were directed toward the water, its frozen form photographed as "ugly."

If you're using this workbook, you probably already have an inkling that not everything you experience can be proven empirically. Try convincing a scientist that chanting "Nam Myoho Renge Kyo" changed the entire dynamic of your relationship with your annoying neighbor and the scientist will scoff, chalking it up to coincidence. But you know your true power, even if nothing can "prove" it. So, let's test out Dr. Emoto's theory for ourselves and see if there's any proof in the ~~pudding~~ H_2O.

instructions

At the beginning of the day, imagine what you would look like if you were a frozen crystal. Base your interpretation on how you feel physically and emotionally. Draw what the crystal formation looks like.

Throughout your day, remember to say only nice things to yourself. (Important: Don't beat yourself up if you catch yourself thinking negative thoughts! Just notice the negative thoughts and let them go.) At the end of the day, return to this exercise and interpret your vibration again in the form of a crystal. Is there any difference? Did the experiment work?

FURTHER READING

THE MIRACLE OF WATER BY DR. MASARU EMOTO

INTENTION

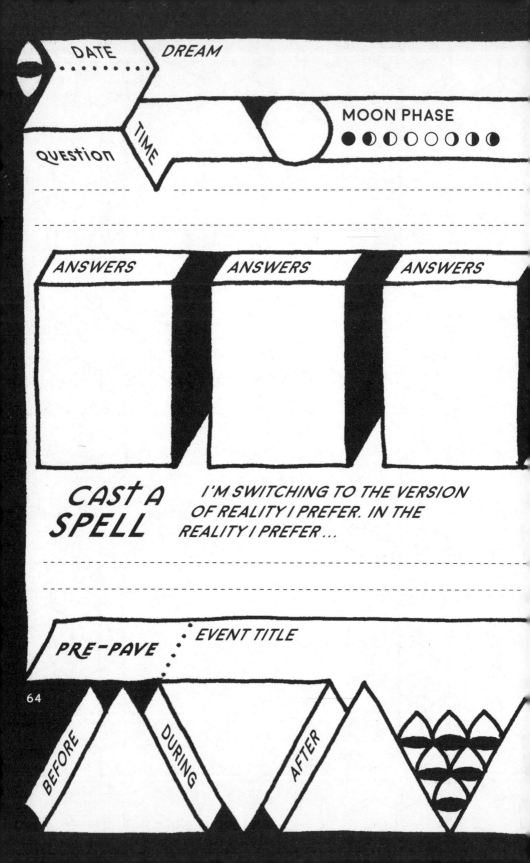

DATE · · · · · · · DREAM

MOON PHASE

Question TIME

- -

- -

ANSWERS   ANSWERS   ANSWERS

CAST A SPELL   I'M SWITCHING TO THE VERSION OF REALITY I PREFER. IN THE REALITY I PREFER...

- -

- -

PRE-PAVE ····· EVENT TITLE

BEFORE   DURING   AFTER

I INTEND

I PRAY

I LOVE

GRATITUDE
IN ADVANCE

I'M SO GRATEFUL

- -

I FORGIVE

- -

- -

- -

- -

*I WANT
TO FEEL*

- -

- -

NOTES & EPIPHANIES

- -

- -

- -

- -

- -

- -

- -

- -

VISIONS & GUIDES

SPELL FOR
GETTING IN THE ZONE

We all love that feeling of being so totally immersed in something that the world slips away, and all that remains is the pleasure of dancing in sync with the present moment. Runners experience this as "runner's high." Performance artists use hula hoops and other props to enter that timeless world of play. Even sitting at our computers, we can get lost in the buzz of completing a task harmoniously and in perfect time.

This rhythm is known as "being in the flow," and it's easier to get there than our minds want us to believe. The trick to getting in this zone is to quiet our minds but busy our bodies. When our thoughts aren't getting in the way of our motion, we enter into the divine pulse of the universe.

You can jump back in the flow of life with a walk outside. Being outside of the comfort zone of our homes wakes us up and places us in an observer position. The movement of our bodies moves our life force energy so it doesn't stagnate in one place. The mind relaxes and opens up to new ideas. Epiphanies and a better mood inevitably ensue.

instructions
Take a walk today, or if you aren't able to walk, find a way to get your body outside and moving in the world. If you are bedridden or housebound, take the journey in your mind.

Make a map of where you went. Note the start and end points, as well whatever good ideas, cool places, favorite parts, friends, cute or beautiful things, magick, mysteries, love, or signs of abundance you noticed.

Measure your mood on a scale of 1-10 before and after your walk.

BEFORE [ ]   AFTER [ ]

FURTHER READING

FLOW BY MIHALY CSIKSZENTMIHALYI

KEY

★ START POINT   🕷 CUTE
◉ END POINT   ⬠ BEAUTIFUL
💬 GOOD IDEA   👽 MAGICK
⟋ COOL PLACE   ⊶ MYSTERIOUS
♥ FAVE PART   🐁 LOVE
☽ FRIEND   💰 ABUNDANCE

GRATITUDE

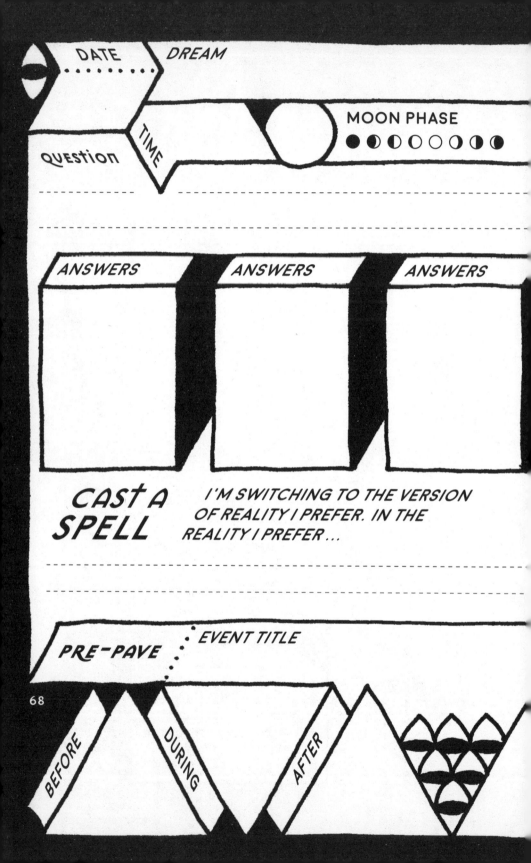

DATE ···· DREAM

MOON PHASE
●●◑◔○○○◐●

QUESTION TIME

ANSWERS

ANSWERS

ANSWERS

CAST A
SPELL

I'M SWITCHING TO THE VERSION
OF REALITY I PREFER. IN THE
REALITY I PREFER...

PRE-PAVE ···· EVENT TITLE

BEFORE DURING AFTER

I INTEND

I PRAY

I LOVE

GRATITUDE
IN ADVANCE

I'M SO GRATEFUL

- -
- -
- -
- -
- -
- -
- -
- -
- -
- -
- -

I FORGIVE

I WANT
TO FEEL

NOTES & EPIPHANIES

- -
- -
- -
- -
- -
- -
- -
- -

VISIONS & GUIDES

SPELL FOR

MAKING DREAMS REALITY

Your waking life is an outpicturing of your internal world, and so is your dream state. Often, your dream state will show you much more exaggerated representations of your current state of mind and being, amplifying subtle or subconscious beliefs, fears, or emotions.

Beyond the symbolism of the objects or events in your dreams, the feelings you feel while these things are taking place are the true key to unlocking the messages from the dream world. Pay attention to how you feel in your dreams; they are showing how you feel deep down.

instructions

1. Set your intention for how you want to feel in your dream.

2. Upon waking, write down what events you can remember.

3. Note how you felt in your dream.

4. Now, do the same thing for your waking life. Before getting out of bed, set your intention. When the day is done, journal the main events, and write how you felt. Did you notice the power of your intention?

FURTHER READING

THE ART OF DREAMING BY CARLOS CASTENADA

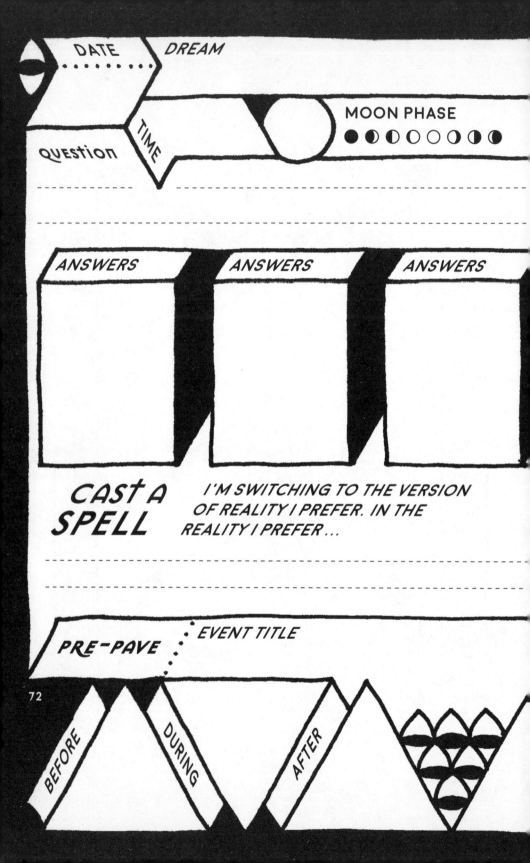

DATE DREAM

QUESTION TIME

MOON PHASE

ANSWERS ANSWERS ANSWERS

CAST A SPELL

I'M SWITCHING TO THE VERSION OF REALITY I PREFER. IN THE REALITY I PREFER...

PRE-PAVE EVENT TITLE

BEFORE DURING AFTER

I INTEND

I PRAY

I LOVE

GRATITUDE in ADVANCE

I'M SO GRATEFUL

- -
- -
- -
- -
- -
- -
- -
- -
- -
- -

I FORGIVE

I WANT
TO FEEL

NOTES & EPIPHANIES

- -
- -
- -
- -
- -
- -
- -

VISIONS & GUIDES

HARNESSING ENERGY

> "Being busy is a form of laziness—lazy thinking
> and indiscriminate action." TIM FERRISS

Pareto's law states that 80% of output results from 20% of the input;
for example, 80% of your income comes from 20% of your work.
Imagine if you could identify the 20% of your efforts that create 80%
of the desired results in your life. How free would you feel if you could
cut out 80% of your activities that don't really contribute much to your
well being?

When you do less, you can emphasize quality over quantity and be very
deliberate about where you place your attention. Where are you placing
your energy, and how much is bringing satisfaction?

instructions

In the space provided, write down everything you do in a day. Next to
each half hour entry, rate the activity on a scale of 1 to 5 stars. One star
means it didn't bring you much joy or value, and 5 stars means you were
thrilled and satisfied.

After you complete your record for a day, look back at your ratings and
evaluate how you spend your time. What would you rather do more
of, and what can you cut out completely? The magick of this exercise
is simple awareness. When you become conscious of your energy, it's
much easier to harness, direct and enjoy.

What would you rather do more of?

What can you cut out completely?

FURTHER READING

THE 4-HOUR WORKWEEK BY TIM FERRISS

AM

12	
:30	
1	
:30	
2	
:30	
3	
:30	
4	
:30	
5	
:30	
6	
:30	
7	
:30	
8	
:30	
9	
:30	
10	
:30	
11	
:30	

PM

12	
:30	
1	
:30	
2	
:30	
3	
:30	
4	
:30	
5	
:30	
6	
:30	
7	
:30	
8	
:30	
9	
:30	
10	
:30	
11	
:30	

CONSCIOUSNESS

ABVПDAПCE & SVCCESS

What is your definition of success? Is it dependent on something outside of you—a certain achievement, standard of living, or income level? Do you believe that once you reach that goal you will be totally fulfilled, no longer seeking anything out of life?

As long as your definition of abundance and success lies outside of yourself, you will always be reaching. No matter what heights you scale, you will always be looking for more.

What this chapter emphasizes is the infinite reservoir of abundance and success you already have. This week, you will unlock the limitless prosperity that surrounds you in every moment. You can finally relax, knowing that you are totally fulfilled. You can bask in the knowledge that all you'll ever want or need, you already have.

DAY	TO NGAF ABOUT	GRATITUDE
DATE		

MEALS

- ☐ _____
- ☐ _____
- ☐ _____
- ☐ _____
- ☐ _____

DAY	TO NGAF ABOUT	GRATITUDE
DATE		

MEALS

- ☐ _____
- ☐ _____
- ☐ _____
- ☐ _____
- ☐ _____

DAY	TO NGAF ABOUT	GRATITUDE
DATE		

MEALS

- ☐ _____
- ☐ _____
- ☐ _____
- ☐ _____
- ☐ _____

DAY	TO NGAF ABOUT	GRATITUDE
DATE		

MEALS

- ☐ _____
- ☐ _____
- ☐ _____
- ☐ _____
- ☐ _____

GRATITUDE	TO NGAF ABOUT	DAY
		DATE
	☐ _____	**MEALS**
	☐ _____	
	☐ _____	
	☐ _____	
	☐ _____	

GRATITUDE	TO NGAF ABOUT	DAY
		DATE
	☐ _____	**MEALS**
	☐ _____	
	☐ _____	
	☐ _____	
	☐ _____	

GRATITUDE	TO NGAF ABOUT	DAY
		DATE
	☐ _____	**MEALS**
	☐ _____	
	☐ _____	
	☐ _____	
	☐ _____	

NOTES

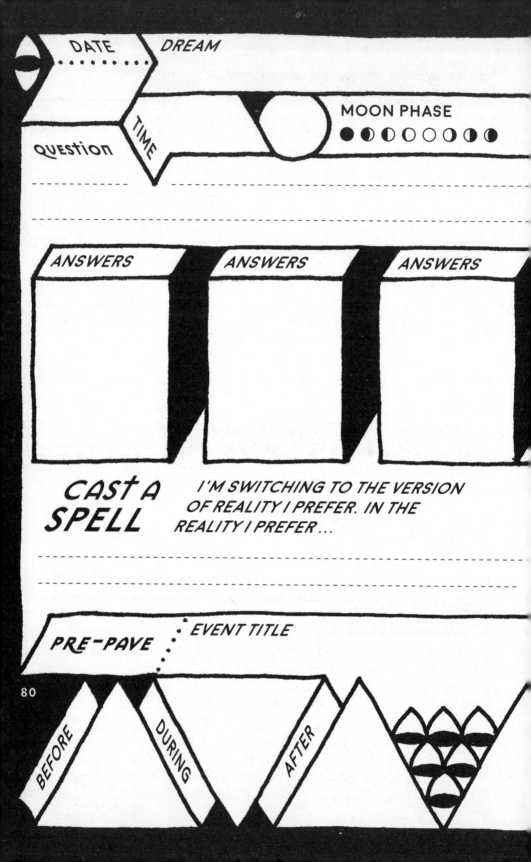

DATE ∙∙∙∙∙∙∙ DREAM

QUESTION TIME

MOON PHASE

ANSWERS ANSWERS ANSWERS

CAST A SPELL

I'M SWITCHING TO THE VERSION OF REALITY I PREFER. IN THE REALITY I PREFER...

PRE-PAVE ∙∙∙ EVENT TITLE

BEFORE DURING AFTER

I INTEND

I PRAY

I LOVE

GRATITUDE
IN ADVANCE

I'M SO GRATEFUL

I FORGIVE

I WANT
TO FEEL

NOTES & EPIPHANIES

VISIONS & GUIDES

SPELL FOR
RECEIVING

> "No offense to Napoleon Hill, the author of the self-help classic on which my title riffs, but the real power is in not thinking. If you want to override your brain's unfortunate habit of leafing through your past and creating a present hologram to match, forget thinking. And start thanking." PAM GROUT

Grout goes on to explain that you don't have to do anything to connect to the energy field that attracts the most extraordinary aspects of life besides simply tune out the voices that tell you otherwise. Replace all of your doubts, fears, and self loathing with "thank you," and you will be on the path to miracles.

instructions

Fill the frame provided with the words "thank you." You don't even have to be thinking about a certain object or experience that you're particularly grateful for. Just write the words "thank you." Write them over and over again. And when your mind starts to wander to something you're definitely not grateful for, tune it back to "thank you." Feel the resonance that comes just from writing the words. Feel the gratitude that flows into your being just from writing the words, and then notice all the things you have to be grateful for that rush to your mind. Replace all other thoughts with thank you. Write it so many times that your thought pattern defaults to it. Take this mental code into your day and thank everything. Then write down the major manifestations you allowed in your life by simply tuning out the thoughts that told you they weren't possible.

MIRACLE LOG

FURTHER READING

THANK AND GROW RICH BY PAM GROUT

MENTAL CODES

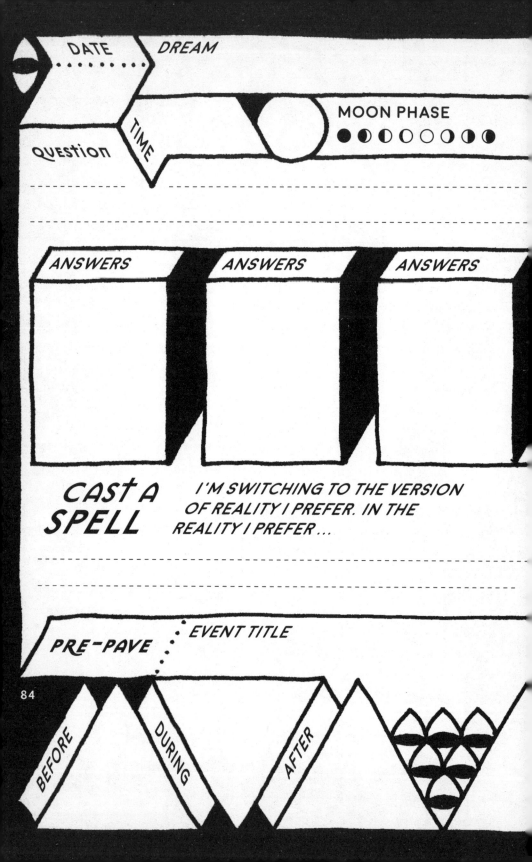

DATE · · · · · · · DREAM

QUESTION TIME

MOON PHASE

ANSWERS ANSWERS ANSWERS

CAST A
SPELL
*I'M SWITCHING TO THE VERSION
OF REALITY I PREFER. IN THE
REALITY I PREFER...*

PRE-PAVE · · · · EVENT TITLE

BEFORE DURING AFTER

I INTEND

I PRAY

I LOVE

GRATITUDE
IN ADVANCE

I'M SO GRATEFUL

- - - - - - - - - - - - - - - - - - - -
- - - - - - - - - - - - - - - - - - - -
- - - - - - - - - - - - - - - - - - - -
- - - - - - - - - - - - - - - - - - - -
- - - - - - - - - - - - - - - - - - - -
- - - - - - - - - - - - - - - - - - - -
- - - - - - - - - - - - - - - - - - - -
- - - - - - - - - - - - - - - - - - - -
- - - - - - - - - - - - - - - - - - - -
- - - - - - - - - - - - - - - - - - - -

I FORGIVE

I WANT
TO FEEL

NOTES & EPIPHANIES

- - - - - - - - - - - - - - - - - - - -
- - - - - - - - - - - - - - - - - - - -
- - - - - - - - - - - - - - - - - - - -
- - - - - - - - - - - - - - - - - - - -
- - - - - - - - - - - - - - - - - - - -
- - - - - - - - - - - - - - - - - - - -
- - - - - - - - - - - - - - - - - - - -

VISIONS & GUIDES

APPRECIATING IN VALUE

A phrase we use often in our work is, "Even when you're saying no, you're saying yes." Influenced by the teachings of Abraham-Hicks, this means that even if you don't want something, if you are giving it attention, you attract more of it. When you focus on how much you don't want something, you create more of it in your life by giving your attention to it, because what you focus on expands. When you notice it, you get more of it. What you resist persists.

On the other hand, if you can find a way to be at peace with what nags you—even going so far as to be grateful for what you do not prefer—you will see that the thing you think is in your way is actually giving you the powerful opportunity to align with your truest and deepest desires.

instructions

Write down something you are definitely *not* grateful for in the space provided, then fill in the chart below to note your level of peace in relationship to the topic. Then come up with as many reasons as possible why you *can* be grateful for that thing, and write them in the blank rectangles. Maybe having to go to the post office is helping you get exercise, or maybe your neighbor's loud music is helping you not overwork yourself. How peaceful do you feel now? Record it below.

BEFORE   AFTER

When you're able to shift your focus to things that you *are* grateful for, you'll notice that what you once thought was a problem is presenting you with a solution.

FURTHER READING

ASK AND IT IS GIVEN BY ESTHER AND JERRY HICKS

WHAT I'M NOT GRATEFUL FOR

GRATITUDE

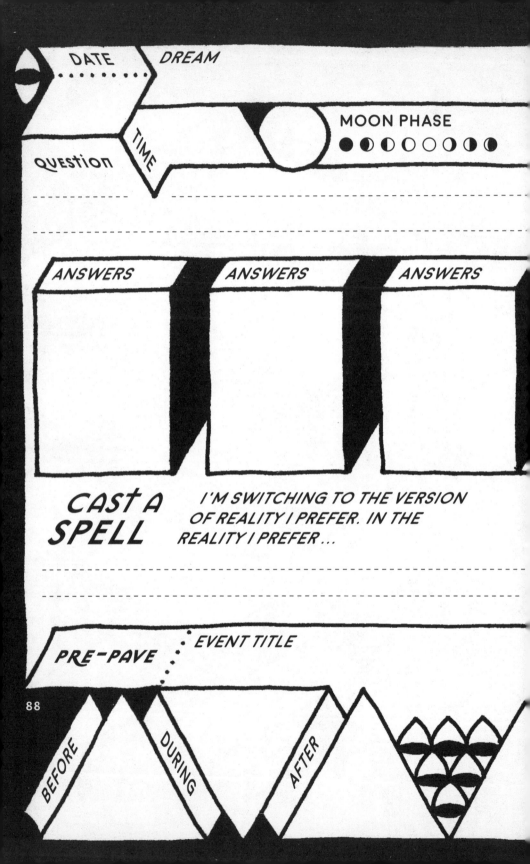

DATE · · · · · · · · DREAM

QUESTION TIME

MOON PHASE
●◑◑◑○◑◑●

ANSWERS ANSWERS ANSWERS

CAST A SPELL

I'M SWITCHING TO THE VERSION OF REALITY I PREFER. IN THE REALITY I PREFER...

PRE-PAVE · · · EVENT TITLE

BEFORE DURING AFTER

I INTEND

I PRAY

I LOVE

GRATITUDE
IN ADVANCE

I'M SO GRATEFUL

- - - - - - - - - - - - - - - - - - - -
- - - - - - - - - - - - - - - - - - - -
- - - - - - - - - - - - - - - - - - - -
I FORGIVE
- - - - - - - - - - - - - - - - - - - -
- - - - - - - - - - - - - - - - - - - -
- - - - - - - - - - - - - - - - - - - -
- - - - - - - - - - - - - - - - - - - -
- - - - - - - - - - - - - - - - - - - -
*I WANT
TO FEEL*
- - - - - - - - - - - - - - - - - - - -
- - - - - - - - - - - - - - - - - - - -
- - - - - - - - - - - - - - - - - - - -

NOTES & EPIPHANIES

- - - - - - - - - - - - - - - - - - - -
- - - - - - - - - - - - - - - - - - - -
- - - - - - - - - - - - - - - - - - - -
- - - - - - - - - - - - - - - - - - - -
- - - - - - - - - - - - - - - - - - - -
- - - - - - - - - - - - - - - - - - - -
- - - - - - - - - - - - - - - - - - - -
- - - - - - - - - - - - - - - - - - - -

VISIONS & GUIDES

SPELL FOR
WEALTH, PRODUCTIVITY AND SUCCESS

"Practice allowing your essential nature to shine by not enforcing judgements on yourself that were imposed by others. Remind yourself that you don't have to do anything: You don't have to be better than anyone else. Give yourself permission to just be. Lighten the burden you carry to be productive, wealthy and successful in the eyes of others."

DR. WAYNE DYER

How much of what you do on a daily basis is to please others? Do you find yourself constantly trying to succeed or achieve? Do you ever feel like you fill your entire day with doing and never get anything done? Or maybe it's not even for others, maybe you're constantly trying to be and do your best only for yourself. But why?

instructions

Take a break from striving today. In the spell candles provided, write lists of the things you think you need to do to be wealthy, successful, and productive today, and then don't do a single one of them! Metaphorically allow the candles to burn, melting away your "to-do" list, one item at a time. This will probably be hard. You will feel useless. Worthless, even. But then you will feel free. Every time your mind tries to tell you that you absolutely must get that thing done, stop and allow yourself to exist for a moment without the expectation of achievement. Don't do anything you don't want to do!

Then, if any of the items call to you–if wild horses can't stop you from performing that task, then you'll know that is your true self carrying out that action, not the version of yourself that thinks you have to. If you simply MUST do something on this list after making the choice not to do any of it, you will know that you are doing that thing simply for the satisfaction of doing it, not because you think it will make you a better person. Then you will be your best self.

FURTHER READING

CHANGE YOUR THOUGHTS, CHANGE YOUR LIFE BY DR. WAYNE DYER

INTENTION

DATE · · · · · · · DREAM

MOON PHASE
●◐●◐○●◐○●

QUESTION   TIME

- -

- -

ANSWERS   ANSWERS   ANSWERS

CAST A   I'M SWITCHING TO THE VERSION
SPELL   OF REALITY I PREFER. IN THE
          REALITY I PREFER...

- -

- -

PRE-PAVE · · · · EVENT TITLE

BEFORE   DURING   AFTER

I INTEND

I PRAY

I LOVE

GRATITUDE
IN ADVANCE

I'M SO GRATEFUL

I FORGIVE

I WANT
TO FEEL

NOTES & EPIPHANIES

VISIONS & GUIDES

�-action

Force, by definition, implies action. One thing is acting upon another, and there's usually some resistance involved. If something is easy, you're not forcing it. It slides right into place; it doesn't require energy.

The opposite of force is ease, and as the *Tao Te Ching* by Lao Tzu explains, "The Tao does nothing, but leaves nothing left undone." The energy that creates worlds is flowing through you. It doesn't need you to interfere in its plan. Notice how when you get out of the way and don't meddle in the happenings of your life, more happens easier, faster, and without complication than when you try to hammer things into place.

For example, say you want upper body strength. If you were forcing it, you might create a rigid workout schedule, go on a diet, and spend hours researching how to improve your form. But if you were allowing upper body strength to come to you, maybe you would start rock climbing for fun. You get so into rock climbing that one day you realize you've been pulling yourself up by your arms, not even noticing that now you have the upper body strength you desired. What if what you wanted to achieve came as a by-product of doing something fun? Let this exercise open your mind to the possibilities of allowing instead of forcing, and see what unfolds.

instructions

Write down something you want to achieve, but have been struggling with. In the block of ice, write what it would look like to try to force it to happen. What kinds of action do you have to take? How does it feel?

Now, imagine allowing your achievement into existence. In the water below the ice, write what fun things might lead you to your achievement, if you were allowing life to flow. How does it feel to allow instead of force?

FURTHER READING

TAO TE CHING BY LAO TZU

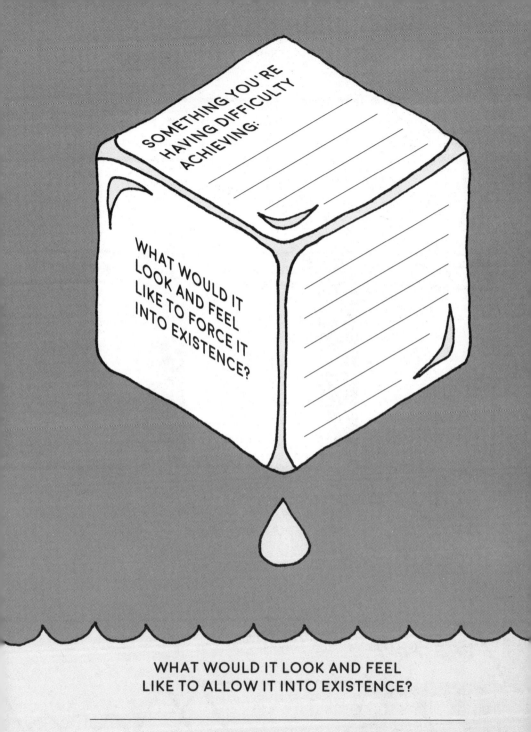

WHAT WOULD IT LOOK AND FEEL
LIKE TO ALLOW IT INTO EXISTENCE?

_____

_____

_____

TRANSMUTATION

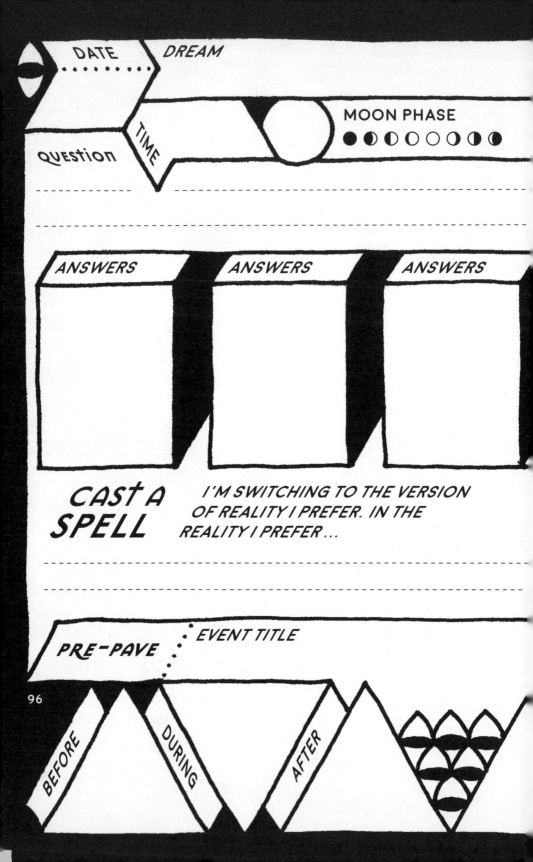

DATE ········ DREAM

MOON PHASE
●●◑◑◑○○◐◑●

QUESTION TIME

ANSWERS ANSWERS ANSWERS

CAST A
SPELL

I'M SWITCHING TO THE VERSION OF REALITY I PREFER. IN THE REALITY I PREFER...

PRE-PAVE ····· EVENT TITLE

96

BEFORE DURING AFTER

I INTEND

I PRAY

I LOVE

GRatitUDE
in ADVAnCE

I'M SO GRATEFUL

I FORGIVE

- - - - - - - - - - - - - - - - - -

- - - - - - - - - - - - - - - - - -

- - - - - - - - - - - - - - - - - -

- - - - - - - - - - - - - - - - - -

- - - - - - - - - - - - - - - - - -

*I WANT
TO FEEL*

- - - - - - - - - - - - - - - - - -

- - - - - - - - - - - - - - - - - -

- - - - - - - - - - - - - - - - - -

- - - - - - - - - - - - - - - - - -

NOTES & EPIPHANIES

- - - - - - - - - - - - - - - - - -

- - - - - - - - - - - - - - - - - -

- -

- -

- -

- -

- -

- -

- -

VISIONS & GUIDES

SPELL FOR
VALIDATION

Do you ever notice yourself caring a little too much about Instagram likes? Or maybe you really want your parents to support your choices? The need for external validation comes as a result of feeling ashamed of ourselves. We feel like we don't measure up to someone else's standards. Maybe we feel like we haven't achieved enough yet or made enough money. When we feel ashamed, we think that praise from other people will help us feel better. But it never will until we address the root of the problem: our shame.

There's no need for deep psychological unearthing to get to the bottom of this. Use a simple pivoting process to start noticing (and switching to) the opposite side of the energetic wave. The opposite of shame is pride, and you can choose to feel proud of yourself right now.

When we deliberately choose to feel proud of ourselves, we start noticing the things we do that we truly are proud of. Getting out of bed, being kind to a stranger, eating a vegetable—there are so many tiny acts we perform each day to be proud of. Today, let, "I'm so proud of myself" be your mental code. Before long, you will start liking yourself so much that you won't need to hear it from anyone else.

instructions
Fill the frame with the words, "I am so proud of myself." Try to really feel the emotion of pride in yourself as you're writing. Notice how empowering it feels to be proud of yourself.

Note one thing you noticed you are proud of yourself for after doing this exercise:

FURTHER READING

MONEY AND THE LAW OF ATTRACTION BY ESTHER AND JERRY HICKS

MENTAL CODES

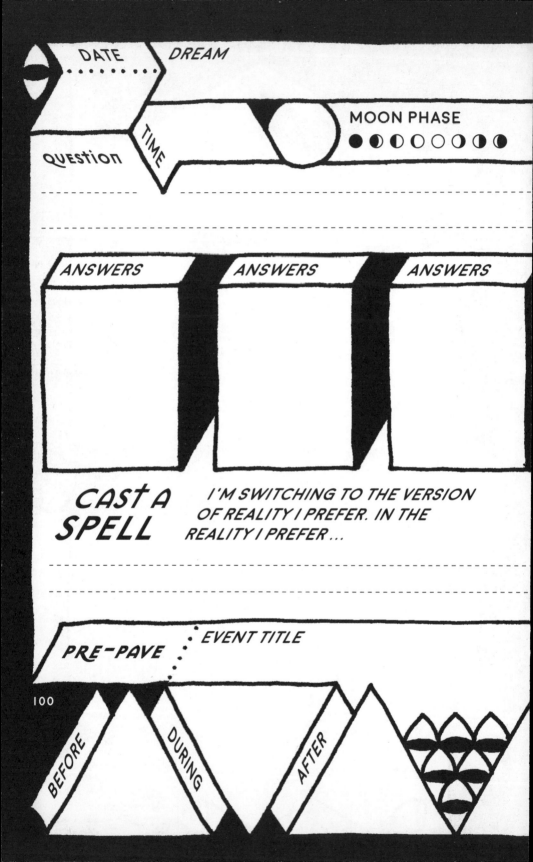

DATE

DREAM

MOON PHASE

Question

TIME

ANSWERS   ANSWERS   ANSWERS

CAST A SPELL   I'M SWITCHING TO THE VERSION OF REALITY I PREFER. IN THE REALITY I PREFER...

PRE-PAVE   EVENT TITLE

BEFORE   DURING   AFTER

I INTEND

I PRAY

I LOVE

GRATITUDE
IN ADVANCE

I'M SO GRATEFUL

I FORGIVE

I WANT
TO FEEL

NOTES & EPIPHANIES

VISIONS & GUIDES

SPELL FOR
GOOD ADVICE

Do you need some solid advice to take your endeavors to the next level? A therapist, guru, life coach, or mentor can uplift and inspire positive change deliberately and consistently. But what if you need the advice right now, or don't have a guide to call on? It's time to use your imagination and your mental collection of heroes.

You have access to infinite intelligence at all times, but sometimes we need a human conduit to make the information accessible. All people know all things at all times, but answering specific questions requires allowing and remembering. And who better to help you remember than a leader you already look up to?

The following channeling process taps into universal wisdom through the voices of people you admire. You may be surprised how much help is already inside you!

instructions

1. What do you need advice about? Write down the question in the central diamond.

2. In the circles provided, write the names of six different people whose advice you would treasure. They can be living or dead, existing in celebrity or obscurity. All that matters is that you trust their perspective and opinion.

3. Now, close your eyes and imagine having a conversation with each person. Ask them the question you have written down. And then quiet your mind and wait for them to speak. Write down their advice in the corresponding rectangles next to their names.

Now you know what to do!

FURTHER READING

THINK AND GROW RICH BY NAPOLEON HILL

CHANNELING

DATE

DREAM

QUESTION

TIME

MOON PHASE

ANSWERS

ANSWERS

ANSWERS

CAST A SPELL

I'M SWITCHING TO THE VERSION OF REALITY I PREFER. IN THE REALITY I PREFER...

PRE-PAVE

EVENT TITLE

BEFORE

DURING

AFTER

I INTEND

I PRAY

I LOVE

GRATITUDE
IN ADVANCE

I'M SO GRATEFUL

- -

I FORGIVE

- -

- -

- -

- -

I WANT
TO FEEL

- -

- -

NOTES & EPIPHANIES

- -

- -

- -

- -

- -

- -

- -

VISIONS & GUIDES

SPELL FOR
infinite ABUNDANCE

"Giving is an esoteric science that never fails to produce results if it is done with love and joy, because the Law will shower you with a multiplied return. But if you tithe (and I really prefer the word 'sharing' to tithing) as a mechanical and calculated method to please God, unload guilt, meet a sense of obligation, and play a bartering game with the Law, no one benefits, not even the receiver. Give with love, joy, and a sense of fun, and the windows of heaven will be thrown open with a blast!" JOHN RANDOLPH PRICE

Money (or how much you have of it), like everything else in the material world, is an indicator of your connection to source—an outpicturing of your inner world. Most people think that they will get money and then feel fulfilled, but the reality is that first you must feel fulfilled and then you will attract money. Money is an indicator of well being, not a source of it.

That's why the science of giving, as John Randolph Price puts it in *The Abundance Book*, works so well. When you give with the knowledge that there is always more than enough and your supply isn't limited by giving it away, the "Law" responds with more. When you understand that the gifts life has for you are limitless, then they are.

instructions
Give something away today. Whether it be your time, your money, your praise or maybe your energy, give it as if there is no limit to your supply. Give it joyfully knowing that you are lucky enough to have tapped into infinite abundance. Give knowing that everything you give to life, it gives back to you (and then some). But don't do it to get something, do it for the sheer joy of sharing the infinite. How does it feel?

FURTHER READING

THE 40-DAY PROSPERITY PLAN BY JOHN RANDOLPH PRICE

TODAY I GAVE

IT FELT

REMOVING BLOCKS

You're getting really good at knowing how you feel in every moment and then directing that emotion with the techniques you used in previous weeks, but there may be some energetic blocks that are harder to overcome than others. If you've been hanging on to something for a long time, the energy of those emotions have a stronger pull over you. The techniques in this chapter will help you dissolve those heavier energetic weights.

Nothing in your life is "simply the way it is." You always have creative control. You always have the power to choose how you feel and the way you look at things. There is no energy that cannot be transmuted and no limit to how good you can feel.

This week's exercises help you look at your core beliefs and ask yourself if you want to keep believing them. If there's something you've been wanting for a long time, but haven't gotten, there's an energetic reason why. If there's a grudge you just can't shake, there's always an alchemical solution. This chapter will help you bring the power of magick to every situation in your life, no matter how dark or overwhelming.

DAY	TO NGAF ABOUT	GRATITUDE
DATE		
MEALS	☐ _____	
	☐ _____	
	☐ _____	
	☐ _____	
	☐ _____	

DAY	TO NGAF ABOUT	GRATITUDE
DATE		
MEALS	☐ _____	
	☐ _____	
	☐ _____	
	☐ _____	
	☐ _____	

DAY	TO NGAF ABOUT	GRATITUDE
DATE		
MEALS	☐ _____	
	☐ _____	
	☐ _____	
	☐ _____	
	☐ _____	

DAY	TO NGAF ABOUT	GRATITUDE
DATE		
MEALS	☐ _____	
	☐ _____	
	☐ _____	
	☐ _____	
	☐ _____	

| GRATITUDE | TO NGAF ABOUT | DAY |
| | | DATE |

	MEALS
☐ _____	
☐ _____	
☐ _____	
☐ _____	
☐ _____	

| GRATITUDE | TO NGAF ABOUT | DAY |
| | | DATE |

	MEALS
☐ _____	
☐ _____	
☐ _____	
☐ _____	
☐ _____	

| GRATITUDE | TO NGAF ABOUT | DAY |
| | | DATE |

	MEALS
☐ _____	
☐ _____	
☐ _____	
☐ _____	
☐ _____	

NOTES

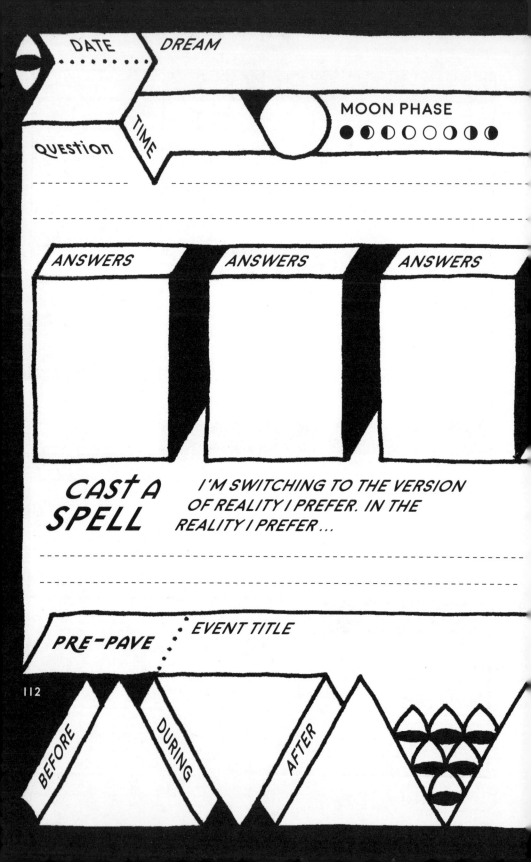

DATE

DREAM

QUESTION

TIME

MOON PHASE

● ◐ ◑ ◒ ○ ◔ ◐ ◖

ANSWERS

ANSWERS

ANSWERS

CAST A
SPELL

I'M SWITCHING TO THE VERSION
OF REALITY I PREFER. IN THE
REALITY I PREFER...

PRE-PAVE

EVENT TITLE

BEFORE

DURING

AFTER

I INTEND

I PRAY

I LOVE

GRatitUDE
in ADVAnCE

I'M SO GRATEFUL

I FORGIVE

- - - - - - - - - - - - - - - - - - - -

- - - - - - - - - - - - - - - - - - - -

- - - - - - - - - - - - - - - - - - - -

- - - - - - - - - - - - - - - - - - - -

- - - - - - - - - - - - - - - - - - - -

I WANT
TO FEEL

- - - - - - - - - - - - - - - - - - - -

- - - - - - - - - - - - - - - - - - - -

NOTES & EPIPHANIES

- - - - - - - - - - - - - - - - - - - -

- - - - - - - - - - - - - - - - - - - -

- - - - - - - - - - - - - - - - - - - -

- - - - - - - - - - - - - - - - - - - -

- - - - - - - - - - - - - - - - - - - -

- - - - - - - - - - - - - - - - - - - -

- - - - - - - - - - - - - - - - - - - -

VISIONS & GUIDES

SPELL FOR
FEELING BETTER

As Abraham-Hicks teaches, your emotions are your guidance system here on earth. They help you know if you are headed in the right direction. When you feel good, you are in alignment with source energy. When you feel bad, something is off. It's as simple as that. When you feel good, life reflects that good feeling and everything you want flows your way. When you feel bad, you push life away. When you feel bad, that is source energy's way of telling you you're off track. "Come back to me," source beckons. It's easy to feel good. When you feel good no matter what, nothing else matters.

instructions
Write a list of your go-to ways to feel good and then do a few of them. Record how you feel before and after. Color in the stars on the left to rate how you feel before the activity, and color the stars to the right of the blank after. Do you feel better now? Do you feel more optimistic about life? As your day goes on, pay attention to how you feel. The moment you start to feel bad, go back to your list and do it until you feel better. After feeling better, does your day start to click into place? Record the positive manifestations that come about as a result of feeling better.

positive manifestations

_____

_____

_____

_____

_____

_____

FURTHER READING

GETTING INTO THE VORTEX BY ESTHER AND JERRY HICKS

1.
2.
3.
4.
5.
6.
7.
8.
9.
10.

CONSCIOUSNESS

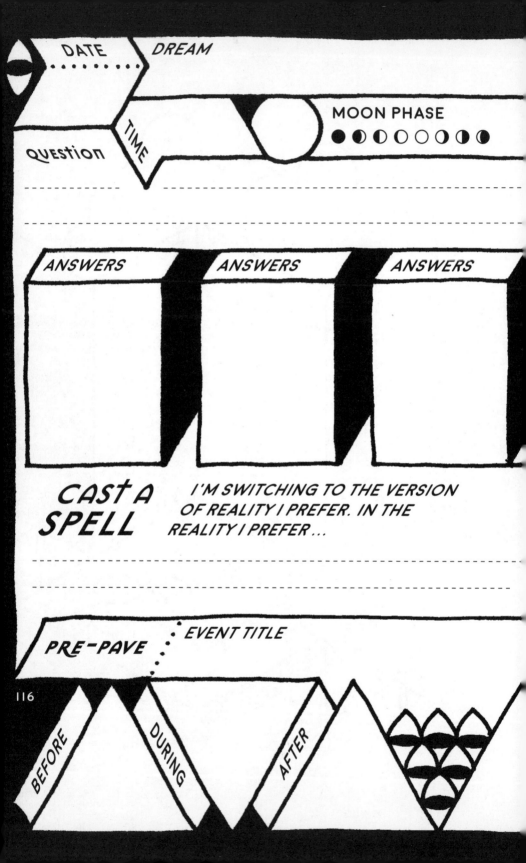

DATE

· · · · · · ·

DREAM

MOON PHASE

Question

TIME

ANSWERS

ANSWERS

ANSWERS

CAST A
SPELL

I'M SWITCHING TO THE VERSION
OF REALITY I PREFER. IN THE
REALITY I PREFER ...

PRE-PAVE

EVENT TITLE

BEFORE

DURING

AFTER

I INTEND

I PRAY

I LOVE

GRATITUDE
IN ADVANCE

I'M SO GRATEFUL

- -
- -
- -

I FORGIVE

- -
- -
- -

I WANT
TO FEEL

- -
- -

NOTES & EPIPHANIES

- -

- -
- -
- -
- -
- -
- -
- -

VISIONS & GUIDES

SPELL FOR
CONNECTION

You think you have problems, but the only problem you ever have is disconnection. When you are disconnected from the infinite version of yourself, you feel something is missing. You might think it's money or a partner or possessions, but as soon as you obtain one of those, you will look for another outside source to fill the infinite hole within. It will never be enough.

You think if you solve your "problem," you will feel better. You think you will feel relieved, happy, fulfilled, or safe. But have you ever noticed that getting what you want never fills you up? That new car smell wears off and you're still the same person. Or you hang out with your crush but the time you had isn't enough and you need more and more and more to fill the void.

There's no certainty in an ever-changing world, and if you allow something outside of you to be your reason for feeling good, you will feel bad when that situation changes. However, if your reason for feeling good is because you know that you are god in human form and that nothing can ever sever the tie you have with the magick of life, you will never have to feel bad no matter what happens (or doesn't happen). If that job falls through and you become destitute and have to live on the streets with your cat on a leash, you will still have access to the infinite love and satisfaction within.

instructions

1. What do I think will make me happy?

2. Why do I think it will make me happy?

3. Now ask your infinite self for advice or opinions on the matter. What do you hear?

FURTHER READING

DIE TO LIVE BY MAHARAJ CHARAN SINGH

1.

2.

3.

CHANNELING

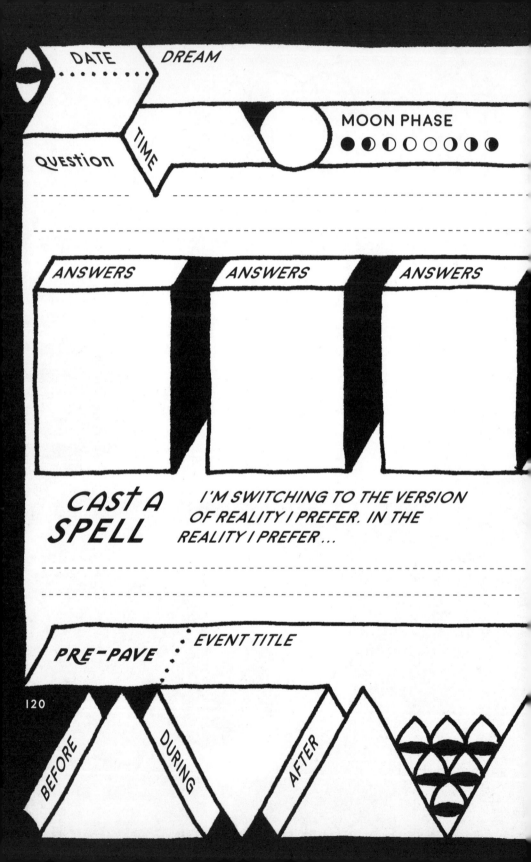

DATE · · · · · · · · DREAM

MOON PHASE
● ◐ ◑ ○ ○ ◑ ◐ ●

QUESTION

TIME

ANSWERS

ANSWERS

ANSWERS

CAST A
SPELL

I'M SWITCHING TO THE VERSION
OF REALITY I PREFER. IN THE
REALITY I PREFER...

PRE-PAVE · · · · · EVENT TITLE

120

BEFORE

DURING

AFTER

I INTEND

I PRAY

I LOVE

GRAtitUDE
in ADVANCE

I'M SO GRATEFUL

- -

I FORGIVE

- -

- -

- -

- -

*I WANT
TO FEEL*

- -

- -

NOTES & EPIPHANIES

- -

- -

- -

- -

- -

- -

- -

- -

VISIONS & GUIDES

SPELL FOR

L⊙VE

Paramhansa Yogananda was an Indian guru and yogi responsible for introducing millions of Indians and Westerners to yoga and meditation in the first half of the 1900s. His most important lesson was to "love god."

But what does it mean to love god? According to many spiritual traditions, god is everything. All that we experience and beyond, including ourselves, is god. So to love god means to love it all. Every single little thing in your life. Every person, every annoying habit, every political outrage and crime against humanity—love it all. And how do you love it? By distancing yourself from your thoughts and reuniting with Who You Really Are.

Learning to love it all is our greatest challenge here on earth. Our minds hate and resist and fear. It's hard to love the bad things people do, or the suffering we witness every day. But to lift the veil of illusion and attain peace of mind (and therefore peace on earth), we must love.

instructions
Think of all the things you hate. All the things that annoy you. All the bad things that happen in your day. And then love them. They are god, and with love they will reveal their true perfection to you.

After each "I love you _____," insert the thing you hate. Then color in the halo of light around the thing you hate, and imagine sending peace and harmony to this thing. God is in everything, and when you practice loving all things, god will be revealed to you.

FURTHER READING

AUTOBIOGRAPHY OF A YOGI BY PARAMAHANSA YOGANANDA

TRANSMUTATION

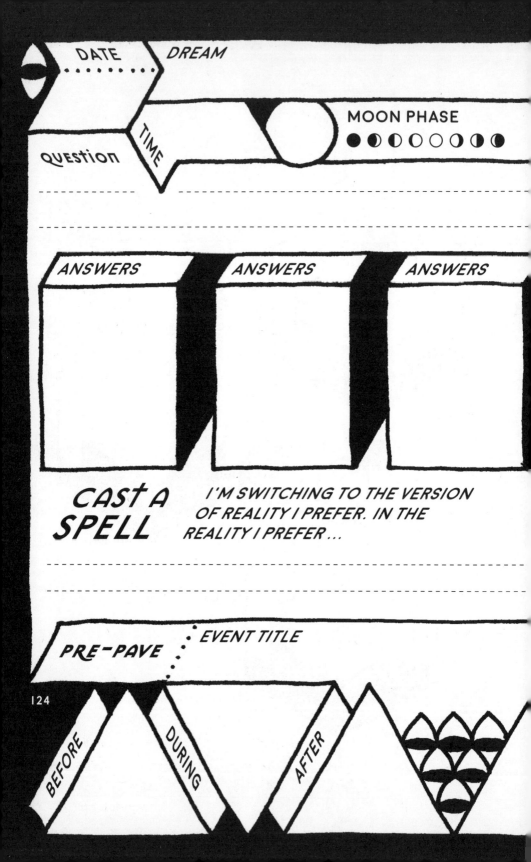

DATE
DREAM
QUESTION
TIME

MOON PHASE
●●●◐○○○◑●●

ANSWERS

ANSWERS

ANSWERS

CAST A
SPELL

I'M SWITCHING TO THE VERSION
OF REALITY I PREFER. IN THE
REALITY I PREFER...

PRE-PAVE   EVENT TITLE

124

BEFORE   DURING   AFTER

I INTEND

I PRAY

I LOVE

GRATITUDE
IN ADVANCE

I'M SO GRATEFUL

- - - - - - - - - - - - - - - - - - - -

- - - - - - - - - - - - - - - - - - - -

- - - - - - - - - - - - - - - - - - - -

- - - - - - - - - - - - - - - - - - - -

I FORGIVE

- - - - - - - - - - - - - - - - - - - -

- - - - - - - - - - - - - - - - - - - -

- - - - - - - - - - - - - - - - - - - -

- - - - - - - - - - - - - - - - - - - -

- - - - - - - - - - - - - - - - - - - -

- - - - - - - - - - - - - - - - - - - -

I WANT
TO FEEL

- - - - - - - - - - - - - - - - - - - -

- - - - - - - - - - - - - - - - - - - -

NOTES & EPIPHANIES

- - - - - - - - - - - - - - - - - - - -

- -

- -

- -

- -

- -

- -

VISIONS & GUIDES

FEARLESSПESS

When we are afraid, it's usually a fear of the unknown. We "don't know" what's going to happen, and that makes us feel uncomfortable and nervous. But what if you did know? What if you knew you never had to worry? You never have to worry because everything is always responding to your inner world. When you line up the energy within, the world has no choice but to respond. Beyond that, you will feel good no matter what happens. When you make the choice to feel good no matter what happens, you don't have to be afraid because you know the outcome doesn't affect your state of being. Practice being at peace despite outcomes and you won't ever have to be afraid again.

instructions

1. Write down what you're afraid of and your fear level associated with that fear.

How can you continue living even if the worst happens?
How can you make peace? Might there even be a silver lining in the worst possible scenario?

2. Write down how you can feel good even if your (often irrational) fears come true. Now that you've made peace with what you don't want to happen, are you less afraid? Has your fear level subsided? Write down your fear level now.

FURTHER READING

THE ESSENTIAL RUMI BY RUMI

TRANSMUTATION

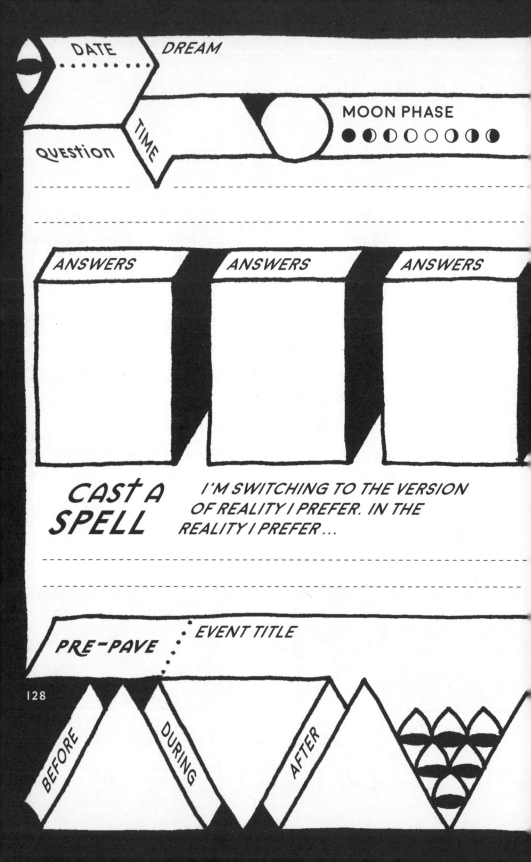

DATE

DREAM

TIME

QUESTION

MOON PHASE

ANSWERS   ANSWERS   ANSWERS

CAST A
SPELL

*I'M SWITCHING TO THE VERSION
OF REALITY I PREFER. IN THE
REALITY I PREFER ...*

PRE-PAVE   *EVENT TITLE*

BEFORE   DURING   AFTER

I INTEND

I PRAY

I LOVE

GRAtitude in ADVANCE

I'M SO GRATEFUL

I FORGIVE

I WANT
TO FEEL

NOTES & EPIPHANIES

VISIONS & GUIDES

SPELL FOR
ENDING SUFFERING

Nichiren Buddhism focuses heavily on the removal of oneself from the roller coaster of life's ups and downs. Rather, practitioners encourage chanting the words, "Nam Myoho Renge Kyo," which translate to "Devotion to the Mystic Law of the Lotus Sutra," or, "Devotion to the Mystic Law of Cause and Effect." Each thought is a cause that immediately creates an effect. Nichiren Buddhists believe that NMRK is the highest thought one may think, which allows the ideal outcome to manifest. When one chants NMRK, all trust is turned over to the universe: "I give up! I resign myself to the flow of life!"

Suffering always stems from attachment. It could be attachment to outcomes, people, circumstances, objects, beliefs, and so on, but suffering always comes from thinking something should be different from how it is. What if we didn't need things to be different, or to be a certain way for us to be happy? What if we could be okay with how life is, because we trust the unfolding of things?

Fill the frame with the words "Nam Myoho Renge Kyo." When your mind starts to wander to that project you need to finish or that conversation you're dreading, tell your mind, "Nam Myoho Renge Kyo." As you write the words, feel how good it feels to know that this is your only responsibility now. Your only "job" is to give in.

NMRK is notorious for bringing about miracles. Be on the lookout today for pinhead solutions and major manifestions and record them below.

FURTHER READING

THE LOTUS SUTRA : A CONTEMPORARY TRANSLATION OF A BUDDHIST CLASSIC
BY GENE REEVES

MENTAL CODES

DATE · · · · · · · · · DREAM

QUESTION TIME

MOON PHASE
●◐◑◑○○◐◑

ANSWERS

ANSWERS

ANSWERS

CAST A
SPELL

I'M SWITCHING TO THE VERSION
OF REALITY I PREFER. IN THE
REALITY I PREFER...

PRE-PAVE · · · EVENT TITLE

132

BEFORE

DURING

AFTER

I INTEND

I PRAY

I LOVE

GRATITUDE
IN ADVANCE

I'M SO GRATEFUL

- -

- -

- -

I FORGIVE

- -

- -

- -

- -

- -

*I WANT
TO FEEL*

- -

- -

NOTES & EPIPHANIES

- -

- -

- -

- -

- -

- -

- -

VISIONS & GUIDES

SPELL FOR

WEIGHTLESSNESS

The things we don't like about other people can help us see where we need to forgive ourselves. When we notice someone else's shortcomings, it is an indicator of what we dislike in our own selves. When we berate someone for being careless, we are calling ourselves out for our own past error. We wouldn't notice the negative behavior if it hadn't first originated in ourselves.

We feel guilty for the things we don't like about ourselves. Often the things we don't like lie below our surface of consciousness: it's easy to notice flaws in others, but a little more difficult to see those same flaws in ourselves. But as the old adage goes, "It takes one to know one."

When you see something you don't like in someone, embrace this opportunity to forgive yourself. If you can truly forgive yourself for the same egregious behavior, you won't be bothered by it in someone else. By giving yourself the love and forgiveness you crave, you also offer it to the person reflecting you. With forgiveness comes freedom, and the delight of a weight lifted!

instructions

1. What is a grudge you're holding? Write the person's name and what the grudge is for.

2. If your grudge had a weight, how much would it weigh?

3. Write down a time when you remember yourself doing the same thing you're begrudging.

4. Forgive yourself for this heinous act by completing the sentence, "I forgive myself for..."

5. Now transfer that forgiveness to the person who hurt you. Finish the sentence, "I also forgive..." with the person's name.

6. Now you can see you were both in need of help and healing. Do you feel a weight lifted? How much does your grudge weigh now?

FURTHER READING

DAILY MEDITATIONS FOR PRACTICING THE COURSE BY KAREN CASEY

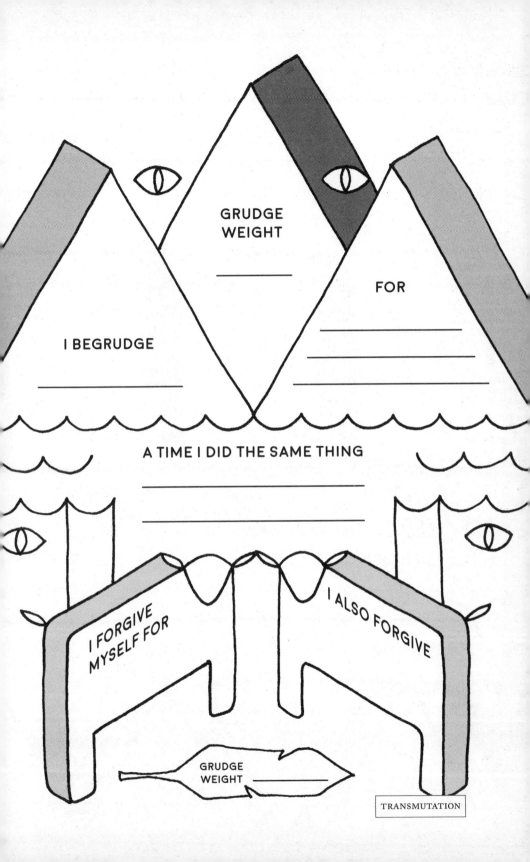

GRUDGE
WEIGHT

_____

FOR

_____

_____

_____

I BEGRUDGE

_____

A TIME I DID THE SAME THING

_____

_____

I FORGIVE
MYSELF FOR

I ALSO FORGIVE

GRUDGE
WEIGHT _____

TRANSMUTATION

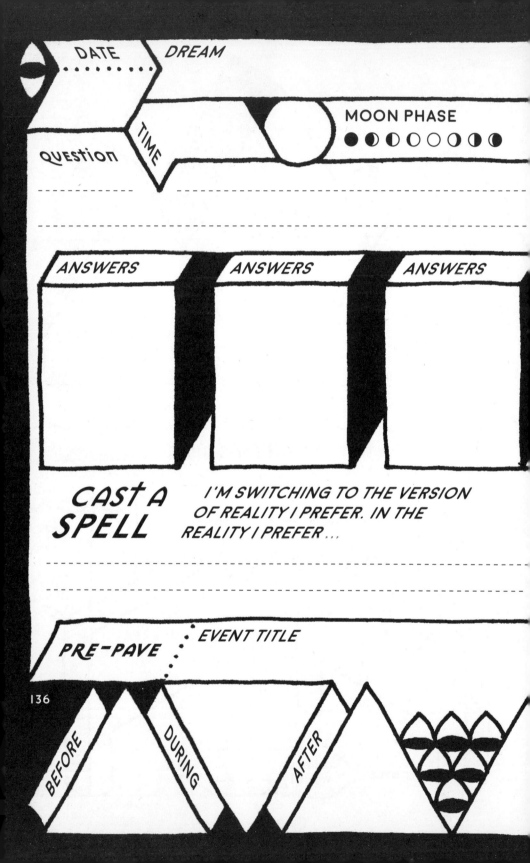

DATE • • • • • • • • DREAM

MOON PHASE
●◐◑○○◑●

QUESTION TIME

- - - - - - - - - - - - - - - - - - -
- - - - - - - - - - - - - - - - - - -

ANSWERS   ANSWERS   ANSWERS

CAST A
SPELL

I'M SWITCHING TO THE VERSION
OF REALITY I PREFER. IN THE
REALITY I PREFER...

- - - - - - - - - - - - - - - - - - -
- - - - - - - - - - - - - - - - - - -

PRE-PAVE •••• EVENT TITLE

136

BEFORE   DURING   AFTER

I INTEND

I PRAY

I LOVE

GRATITUDE
IN ADVANCE

I'M SO GRATEFUL

I FORGIVE

I WANT
TO FEEL

NOTES & EPIPHANIES

VISIONS & GUIDES

SPELL FOR
TRANSCENDENCE

There is an aspect of you that thinks thoughts. It judges and resists everything around you. It decides yes or no, right or wrong. There is also an aspect of you that witnesses those thoughts–your higher self.

When we forget to observe our thoughts from the perspective of our higher selves, we can start to believe that we ARE our thoughts and even worse–that our thoughts are "true." When we are identified with these thoughts, we follow them. We expend a lot of our energy wondering about what ifs. However, when we zoom out and notice the thoughts (and notice the noticing), we realize we don't have to chase every thought that passes through. When we simply watch our thoughts instead of follow them down rabbit holes, we can bring lasting peace to our lives.

Use the process below to embody your observer self. Notice that simply becoming aware of this perspective will bring forth a sense of calm bliss. Next time something bothers you, rather than getting wrapped up in the event, assume the observer perspective and see what kind of insights this awareness can bring to the situation.

instructions

1. Draw an abstract representation of what your thoughts look like in your mind.

2. When you imagined your thoughts in your mind just now, who or what was doing the observing?

3. From where are the thoughts being observed?

4. How does this perspective feel?

5. Now that you have changed your point of view to observer, take a look at your thoughts again. Do the thoughts slow down? Do they fall into a beautiful formation? Draw a visual representation of your energy after working through this process.

FURTHER READING

THE BOOK: ON THE TABOO AGAINST KNOWING WHO YOU ARE BY ALAN WATTS

FREEDOM

....

With the end of your 31-day journey in sight, make plans for your continued success. As you take what you've learned into the future, always remember that you are not your body. You are not your thoughts or emotions. You are not a designer or a writer or an artist or a banker or a real estate agent or any other descriptive label. You are awareness itself creating through the conduit of the human experience. You simply *are*. Keep this truth with you always and you will always be free.

DAY	TO NGAF ABOUT	GRATITUDE
DATE		
MEALS	☐ _____	
	☐ _____	
	☐ _____	
	☐ _____	
	☐ _____	

DAY	TO NGAF ABOUT	GRATITUDE
DATE		
MEALS	☐ _____	
	☐ _____	
	☐ _____	
	☐ _____	
	☐ _____	

DAY	TO NGAF ABOUT	GRATITUDE
DATE		
MEALS	☐ _____	
	☐ _____	
	☐ _____	
	☐ _____	
	☐ _____	

DAY	TO NGAF ABOUT	GRATITUDE
DATE		
MEALS	☐ _____	
	☐ _____	
	☐ _____	
	☐ _____	
	☐ _____	

| GRATITUDE | TO NGAF ABOUT | DAY |
| | | DATE |

MEALS

- [ ] _____
- [ ] _____
- [ ] _____
- [ ] _____
- [ ] _____

| GRATITUDE | TO NGAF ABOUT | DAY |
| | | DATE |

MEALS

- [ ] _____
- [ ] _____
- [ ] _____
- [ ] _____
- [ ] _____

| GRATITUDE | TO NGAF ABOUT | DAY |
| | | DATE |

MEALS

- [ ] _____
- [ ] _____
- [ ] _____
- [ ] _____
- [ ] _____

NOTES

_____
_____
_____
_____
_____
_____

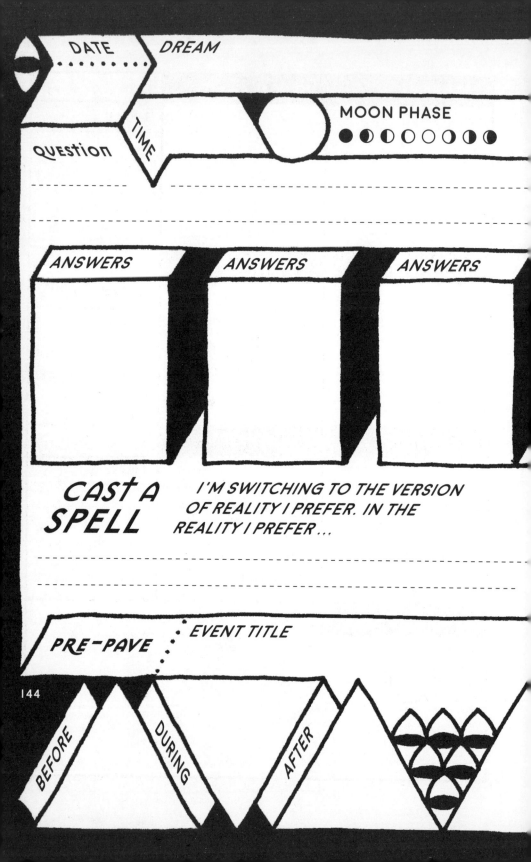

DATE •••••••• DREAM

QUESTION TIME

MOON PHASE

ANSWERS ANSWERS ANSWERS

CAST A
SPELL

I'M SWITCHING TO THE VERSION
OF REALITY I PREFER. IN THE
REALITY I PREFER...

PRE-PAVE ••••• EVENT TITLE

144

BEFORE DURING AFTER

I INTEND

I PRAY

I LOVE

GRATITUDE
IN ADVANCE

I'M SO GRATEFUL

I FORGIVE

I WANT
TO FEEL

NOTES & EPIPHANIES

VISIONS & GUIDES

SPELL FOR
ENLIGHTENMENT

"A lot of people try to counteract the 'I am not good enough' with 'I am good
enough.' In other words, they take the opposite and they try to invest it. That
still keeps the world at the level of polarities. The art is to go behind the
polarities. So the act is to go not to the world of 'I am good' to counteract 'I
am bad,' or 'I am lovable' as opposed to 'I am unlovable.' But go behind it to 'I
am.' I am. I am. And 'I am' includes the fact that I do crappy things and I do
beautiful things and I am. That includes everything and I am." RAM DASS

We live in the world of duality. We can't have rich without poor. We
can't have knowing without ignorance. We can't have happiness without
sadness. Your emotional highs are only as powerful as your lows. When
you ride the rollercoaster of duality, you can get seasick from all the ups
and downs.

We can transcend duality and return to the peace of oneness with the
universe. You aren't good or bad; you just are. The circumstances in your
life just are. They aren't good or bad. They exist. When you are able to
observe yourself and your life experience without judgement clouding
your perception, you feel at peace with everything that is.

instructions
Fill the frame with the words "I AM." Try breathing in as you write "I"
and breathing out as you write "AM." Continue until you fill the page.
Measure your light level before and after, using the sun charts below.

BEFORE AFTER

If your mind tries to put something after "I AM," don't let it. You're
nothing and everything all at once and one word or phrase could never
describe who or what you are. You are, and that's enough.

FURTHER READING

BE HERE NOW BY RAM DASS

MENTAL CODES

DATE · · · · · · · · · · DREAM

QUESTION TIME

MOON PHASE
● ◐ ◑ ◒ ○ ◐ ◑

ANSWERS

ANSWERS

ANSWERS

CAST A SPELL

I'M SWITCHING TO THE VERSION
OF REALITY I PREFER. IN THE
REALITY I PREFER...

PRE-PAVE · · · · EVENT TITLE

BEFORE

DURING

AFTER

I INTEND

I PRAY

I LOVE

GRATITUDE
IN ADVANCE

I'M SO GRATEFUL

- -

- -

I FORGIVE

- -

- -

- -

- -

- -

I WANT
TO FEEL

- -

- -

NOTES & EPIPHANIES

- -

- -
- -
- -
- -
- -
- -
- -

VISIONS & GUIDES

LiFE DESiGn

Technology is a tool, and it can be utilized in both positive and negative ways. This applies especially to our mobile devices, the ubiquitous, anxiety-producing miniature computers that we all love (and sometimes hate). What if we could skew the ratio more towards love and feel a little less addicted to scrolling?

The answer to falling in love with your technology (and yourself) is to be a creator instead of a consumer. It can be draining to wistfully look at everyone else's life and compare what's lacking in ours. But we can choose to set the bar instead of trying to meet it.

What's the goal of social sharing? For some the goal is accolades or validation, but what if you use the magnificent tools technology provides as a way of documenting all that is good (or that you want more of) in your reality?

The practice of documenting what you want more of puts you in a mode of looking for what you want to see. And when you look for reasons to celebrate life, you find them! This is magick in its truest form: you intend to create something, then you look for evidence of that creation and document it.

instr_uctions
Use the space provided to create a storyboard for the movie of your life. What shots will you be looking to capture? What is the mood or message of your documentary? What's the moral of the story? As you move throughout your day, keep an eye out for all that you want to see in your life and document it. It doesn't have to be a movie. It can be photos, words or even your own illustration. Whatever it is you want, *look for it*, and then document when you see it.

FUR†HER_ READiΠG

INEVITABLE BY KEVIN KELLY

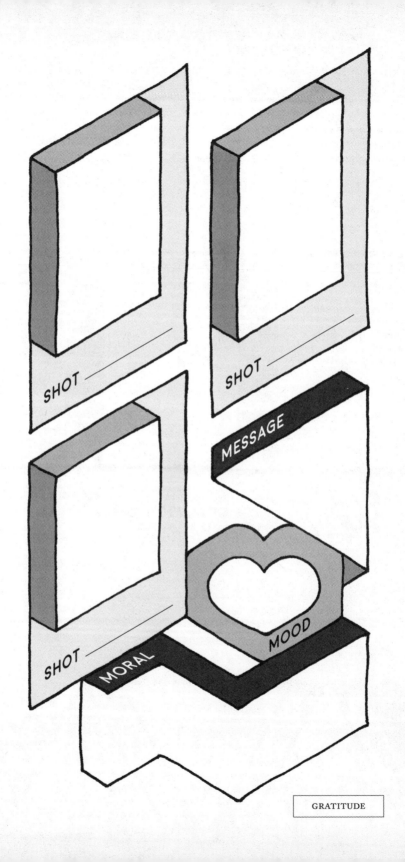

SHOT

SHOT

SHOT

MESSAGE

MORAL

MOOD

GRATITUDE

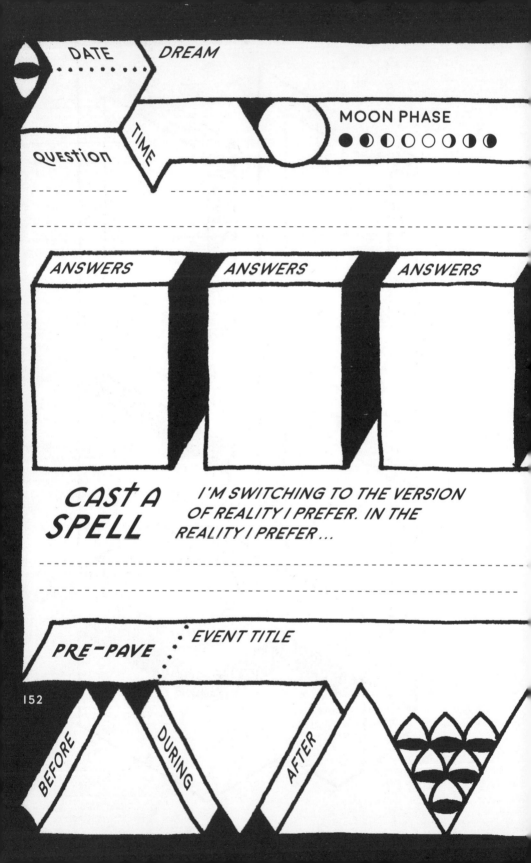

DATE · · · · · · · · · DREAM

MOON PHASE
●◑◑○○○◐◑

QUESTION   TIME

ANSWERS

ANSWERS

ANSWERS

CAST A SPELL   *I'M SWITCHING TO THE VERSION OF REALITY I PREFER. IN THE REALITY I PREFER ...*

PRE-PAVE   EVENT TITLE

BEFORE

DURING

AFTER

I INTEND

I PRAY

I LOVE

GRATITUDE IN ADVANCE

I'M SO GRATEFUL

I FORGIVE

I WANT TO FEEL

NOTES & EPIPHANIES

VISIONS & GUIDES

LASTING SUCCESS

Now that you've worked through 30 exercises in this book, you've probably enjoyed some more than others. Some were probably very effective while others not as much. Every person is different and each technique, process, and mental code speaks differently to all.

What you've also probably caught onto is that which process you choose is not nearly as important as your devotion to the process. When you really do the work, you see the results. When you don't resonate with a particular process, it can be difficult to see or feel results.

instructions

Reflect on the past month and take note of your favorite and most effective processes. Which one was the hardest? What category do you lean towards? What do you want to work on? Use this knowledge to create your own techniques based on what works for you.

FURTHER READING

THE BOOK OF SECRETS BY OSHO

CATEGORIES

GRATITUDE
MENTAL CODES
CHANNELING
CONSCIOUSNESS
INTENTION
TRANSMUTATION
VISUALIZATION

EFFECTIVE

WORK ON

FAVORITE

HARDEST

MICROCOSM·PUBLISHING

MICROCOSM PUBLISHING is Portland's most diversified publishing house and distributor with a focus on the colorful, authentic, and empowering. Our books and zines have put your power in your hands since 1996, equipping readers to make positive changes in their lives and in the world around them. Microcosm emphasizes skill-building, showing hidden histories, and fostering creativity through challenging conventional publishing wisdom with books and bookettes about DIY skills, food, bicycling, gender, self-care, and social justice. What was once a distro and record label was started by Joe Biel in a bedroom and has become among the oldest independent publishing houses in Portland, OR. We are a politically moderate, centrist publisher in a world that has inched to the right for the past 80 years.

Global labor conditions are bad, and our roots in industrial Cleveland in the 70s and 80s made us appreciate the need to treat workers right. Therefore, our books are MADE IN THE USA.

What is School of Life Design?

School of Life Design (SoLD) is a curriculum for accessing the Now, training attention and subverting social constructs. Combining the principles of design with elements of magick, meditation, and manifestation, SoLD makes interactive guides for harnessing the creative power of thought.

Founded in 2010 by Kelly Cree and Jessica Mullen, School of Life Design (SoLD) is a curriculum utilizing the principles of design as a framework for shaping life experience. **Gratitude** is the use of *emphasis*: focus on what you like and what you want more of. **Mental codes** (or mantras) create peaceful mental *rhythm*. **Consciousness** is the *balance* of doing, thinking, feeling, and being. **Intention** is the purposeful *movement* of energy. **Visualization** generates new *patterns* of thought and expectation. **Transmutation** creates joy out of the *contrast* of pain. **Channeling** reveals the *unity* and connectedness of all things.

When used deliberately, these tools enable you to design and experience the reality you prefer. In each moment, you are faced with a design decision: where do you focus your awareness? With daily practice of SoLD's ever-evolving methodology for attention training, you will experience the manifestations, synchronicities, and miracles you desire. Design your reality instead of the other way around; only you are the creator of you.

Learn more at
www.schooloflifedesign.com